Lifeguard Training:

Principles and Administration

A Project of the Council
For National Co-operation in Aquatics

Editorial Committees

First Edition: ROLLAND HILL, CHAIRMAN

GORDON T. HOWES

RICHARD L. BROWN (deceased)

Second Edition: GORDON T. HOWES

LIFEGUARD TRAINING: PRINCIPLES AND ADMINISTRATION

Revised Edition

Illustrations by NANCY R. DeLONG

ASSOCIATION PRESS • NEW YORK

Lifeguard Training: Principles and Administration

•

Copyright © 1968 by
Council for National Co-operation in Aquatics

•

Association Press, 291 Broadway, New York, N. Y.   10007

•

Revised Edition

Publisher's stock number: 1694
Library of Congress catalog card number: 68-9312

2

Printed in the United States of America

FOREWORD: COUNCIL FOR NATIONAL CO-OPERATION IN AQUATICS

Purpose

The purpose of the Council for National Co-operation in Aquatics (CNCA) is to provide a setting in which official representatives of *national organizations* conducting or promoting aquatic activities can come together to:

(1) report on individual agency programs, plans and projects,

(2) share and discuss common problems,

(3) plan ways of working together on agreed-upon projects, and

(4) help advance the field of aquatics.

It is the hope that this planning and working together on appropriate and well-defined tasks will bring about a greater understanding among agencies and make it possible to serve a larger number of people more effectively. Such co-operative efforts, added to the independent work carried on continuously by the various agencies, should help advance the entire field of aquatics.

Membership

Membership shall consist of co-operating *national organizations* that meet the following requirements:

(1) express an interest in and desire to support the purpose of the Council,

5

(2) have membership constituencies or are Federal agencies involved in the promotion of aquatics,

(3) conduct or participate in aquatic programs, or have aquatic facilities and equipment to operate,

(4) employ professional help and use volunteer leadership in aquatics.

Co-operating groups:

> Amateur Athletic Union of the United States
> American Association for Health, Physical Education,
>   and Recreation
> American Camping Association
> American National Red Cross
> American Public Health Association
> American Recreation Society
> Athletic Institute, Inc.
> Boy Scouts of America
> Boys' Clubs of America
> Camp Fire Girls, Inc.
> Division for Girls' and Women's Sports, AAHPER
> National Board of the YWCA
> National Catholic Camping Association
> National Collegiate Athletic Association
> National Council of YMCA's
> National Federation of State High School Athletic Associations
> National Jewish Welfare Board
> National Recreation and Park Association
> National Safety Council
> National Swimming Pool Institute
> National YMCA Aquatic Committee
> Underwater Society of America
> United States Office of Education
> United States Power Squadron
> United States Public Health Service
> Women's National Aquatic Forum

Additional information concerning the CNCA can be obtained by writing to 1201 16th Street, N.W., Washington, D. C. 20036.

INTRODUCTION

For the past fifty years there have been programs of training in individual skills for those desiring to be known as "Life Savers." These have been provided by the American National Red Cross, YMCA's and others in this field. This is highly commendable and reflects well on those fine organizations that have provided such training programs for individuals in this country. There has been a gap, however, between the training of selected individuals in skills related to the lifeguard's job and training in the specifics of being a part of a lifeguard crew. It is hoped that this wealth of material gleaned from many sources across the nation in the field of lifeguard training and administration will help fill the gap so that lifeguards can receive training both in individual skills and team operational techniques to enable them to do their job efficiently and, on more and more occasions, successfully.

7

Those concerned with securing lifeguards and then training them in methods and techniques appropriate to the situation in which the guards are to be employed should find in these pages the very material they need to set up their own programs of training which will be "tailor made" for their special needs. The Council for National Co-operation in Aquatics (CNCA) has produced this guidebook as a service to those faced with the problems of recruiting, training, operating and administering lifeguard facilities across the land. The administrators of every public pool, organizational pool or beach facility of any nature should be able to point with pride to their effective lifeguard system. It should reflect care in selecting personnel, concern for the most efficient methods and consideration through proper administration of the particular swimming facility being observed. This manual should help.

The materials for this book have been gleaned from many sources across the country, and have been compiled by several writers. Those contributing directly as authors of chapters and sections of copy include the following:

Rolland Hill, ARC, Newark, N. J.

Walter Jeff, ARC, Utica, N. Y.

Larry Good, Temple University, Philadelphia, Pa.

Lee L. Starr, Park Dept., N. Y. C.

Gordon T. (Mike) Howes, ARC, Trenton, N. J.

Henry F. Pohl, Ramapo Regional H. S., Franklin Lakes, N. J.

Thomas D. Miller, ARC, Miami, Fla.

Alexander Houston, ARC, Boston, Mass.

Lt. Arthur Schultz (ret.), Police Emergency Squad, Jersey City, N. J.

Lt. Eugene Olaff, State Police, Trenton, N. J.

Trooper Arnold Kleeberg, State Police, Trenton, N. J.

Robert E. Sorge, U. S. Military Academy, West Point, N. Y.

James F. Stern, Great Lakes Biochemical Co., Milwaukee, Wis.

To these and the hosts of others who have examined and made helpful comments as this manuscript was developed, the CNCA expresses its grateful thanks. It typifies the slogan of the Council for National Co-operation in Aquatics so well—"Progress through Co-operation."

E. E. HOISINGTON, PAST CHAIRMAN, CNCA

CONTENTS

SECTION I—PERSONNEL

SECTION II—OPERATIONS

SECTION III—ADMINISTRATION

LIST OF ILLUSTRATIONS

THE TEN COMMANDMENTS OF A LIFEGUARD

1. A lifeguard is vigilant.
   - He will not look for glory in credit for rescues made.
   - He will protect all patrons from the hazards in his area.

2. A lifeguard will prevent accidents.
   - He will protect individuals from their own weaknesses and inabilities.

3. A lifeguard will conduct himself so as to bring credit to his organization.
   - He will never abuse any invested authority.
   - He will reflect dignity associated with saving lives.

4. A lifeguard will be a good subordinate employee.
   - He will work as a member of the team and welcome supervision.

5. A lifeguard's appearance will be a credit to himself and representative of his organization.
   - He will keep his quarters, gear and skills in excellent condition.

6. A lifeguard will keep cool and exercise good judgment in emergencies.
   - He will always take equipment or a flotation device on a rescue attempt.

7. A lifeguard is trustworthy.
   - He is prompt in reporting to duty station.
   - He maintains constant surveillance.
   - He never leaves duty station when hazards exist.

8. A lifeguard is always ready.
   - Condition of "readiness" will be in evidence by constant physical training, practice of skills and use of equipment.

9. A lifeguard will feel the responsibility of his mission.

10. A lifeguard will be progressive.
    - He will constantly seek new and better ways to improve his skills, equipment and profession.

SECTION I

PERSONNEL

1

THE JOB OF THE LIFEGUARD

The major responsibility of the lifeguard is to protect the life and well-being of each person using the aquatic facilities. The well-trained guard will do this by preventing people from getting into situations that endanger themselves or others. When this fails he must be prepared to plan and effect a rescue with the utmost speed and efficiency. The principles behind all lifeguarding are the prevention of accidents before they happen, and a quick, simple, safe rescue if an accident does occur. It has often been said, "A good lifeguard seldom has to get wet."

To be a good lifeguard a person must be physically fit and mentally alert. He must be well trained and have a deep-seated conviction that his job is important. He must be mature enough to recognize and appreciate the vital nature of his responsibility. He should have a sense of loyalty to his organization and respect for his superiors. The good guard will, in turn, have the respect of his superiors and the public.

The lifeguard, in many instances, will be expected to assume other duties beyond pure lifeguarding. These may include such things as cleaning the beach or deck areas, rendering first aid, keeping rescue equipment in its proper place and in good repair, placing guard stands in position and retiring them at the end of the day. He may also be called upon to test the water, operate a filter system and vacuum systems at a pool. He may have to put up cabanas, beach chairs or umbrellas. These duties and others in many cases are part of the lifeguard's job, especially at smaller pools and beaches. However, these extra jobs should be done only when he is not on guard duty or when there is another guard to take the responsibility for his area. A lifeguard cannot be expected to do a safe job of guarding when his mind and body are engaged in some other activity. Lifeguarding is a full-time job.

At many pools and beaches, part of a lifeguard's on-the-job time may also be scheduled for swimming and lifesaving instruction, or for competitive swimming and diving programs. It is not unusual for a pool employee's job to be a combined lifeguard-instructor position. The morning "Learn to Swim Campaign" classes with lifeguards serving as instructors or assisting authorized instructors is a highlight of many pool programs. Lifeguards who have been competitive swimmers or divers can frequently render valuable assistance in organizing, conducting or officiating competitive meets.

With the exception of agency-operated indoor pools and some pools and beaches in Florida and southern California, the job of a lifeguard is a seasonal one. Even in the warmer climate, with year 'round bathing areas, the number of guards employed at any one time will be determined by the patronage and weather conditions.

There is little excuse for not maintaining maximum lifeguard coverage and protection. Pool operators have learned that it is wise to maintain a roster of qualified persons who can serve in the event of an emergency.

Most lifeguards are paid a weekly or seasonal salary, part-time staff on a daily basis, with relief or substitute guards on an hourly basis when they work.

The salary for lifeguard work should be in line with the prevailing or established pay scale for the year or the area. It would be well to remember that efficient and effective guards are not a luxury but a necessity.

Lifeguard work at most agency, privately operated and municipal facilities is generally on a forty- to forty-eight-hour-week basis. In many instances where more than one lifeguard is involved, the work week may be less per lifeguard because of a staggered schedule. At public and private facilities, a full complement of lifeguards is usually planned for weekends and holidays. The on-duty time is equalized with off-duty compensatory time during the week. Staff members at many agencies who do some lifeguarding as part of their overall job can't remember when they put in as little as a forty-hour-week. These are usually the dedicated professionals on a straight salary basis. A lifeguard should be told and given a written work schedule indicating the time and place his job begins. Punctuality is imperative. The lifeguard should arrive at the facility or his post in ample time to change clothes, don the suit or uniform required and be ready to begin work at the specified hour. The work schedule should also indicate the time off for meals, for relief, for a change in stations, for practice sessions or drills and for other duties.

Lifeguards should be aware of where they fit into the total operational procedure. On large beach patrols, there is usually a Chart or Table of Organization and Administration. Titles used in this "chain of command" will vary. Officer of the Day, Lieutenant, Captain, Chief, Superintendent are a few of the more commonly used titles. At swimming pools, lifeguards may become familiar with these same titles or possibly just Captain or Pool Manager.

In most beach patrols and other organizations employing large numbers of lifeguards, uniformity of dress is important. As a matter of personal pride, all lifeguards will keep themselves and their uniforms clean and neat at all times and will wear same *only* when on duty. In addition to trunks or a suit and a whistle, a lifeguard's uniform list may also include "T" shirts, a jacket, sunglasses, a helmet, emblems (Departmental, Red Cross, YMCA, Boys' Club, etc.). These items may be issued to the lifeguards or they may be required to purchase some or all. At indoor facilities, the minimum uniform should be nothing less than a pair of trunks or a suit with an appropriate emblem and a warning whistle attached to a neck cord (worn at all times when on duty).

Suggested Prerequisites for Lifeguard Training

These are suggested minimum requirements for admittance into a lifeguard training course:

1. Age eighteen years—male or female

2. Physical examination
   a) Normal hearing
   b) Good uncorrected vision—the potential guard should be able to see facial expressions of persons at the furthest extremes of the swimming area without glasses. A lifeguard should never wear contact lenses.
   c) Normal heart, lungs and reflexes
   d) No disabling deformities or conditions
   e) Physician's opinion: Is the applicant physically and mentally fit to be a lifeguard?
   f) Five feet, six inches tall—150 lbs.—male
   g) Five feet, eight inches tall—135 lbs.—female

3. Able to swim 440 yards in open water in twelve minutes

4. Holds a current or valid Red Cross or YMCA Senior Lifesaving certificate or its equivalent

5. Supplies references attesting to maturity and judgment, reliability and character

2

PERSONAL HEALTH, FITNESS AND IN-SERVICE TRAINING

The effectiveness of a guard will be in direct proportion to his ability to maintain a high degree of fitness. The physical and mental strain peculiar to this type of work demands fast recuperation. Only a person in good health can qualify.

Physical Considerations

The personal habits of a guard should ensure a minimum of eight hours' sleep each night and at least one full-course meal a day. In the interest of alertness, a guard should abstain from alcoholic beverages prior to and during work. Smoking on the job is usually covered by rules of conduct set up for each specific facility.

The rigors of exposure to the elements can be met by the rule of common sense. The disregard for effects of over-exposure to the sun, especially during the first days on the job, has given many a lifeguard a sad experience. Severe burns in the areas behind the knees and on the insteps of the feet can make walking very painful for a few days. The most effective prevention of sunburn lies in limiting the time of initial exposure. Dullness can be prevented by use of good head and eye protection. The use of a helmet, light-colored cap or umbrella for the head and good dark-colored sunglasses for the eyes is highly recommended. Sunglasses ground to prescription are also recommended for those who normally wear glasses.

Protection against the other extreme, cold, damp weather, is also important. Warm, loose, rain-resistant, easy-to-shed clothing should be included in a lifeguard's personal wardrobe. Protection of the warmth of the feet should not be overlooked. It is also important to be concerned about the health of the feet over the season.

The environmental factors in a swimming area often cause minor wounds. Be especially careful about their care; exposure to dampness often prevents healing and could result in infection. The use of talcum powder to keep the feet dry, especially between the toes, will assist in prevention of skin irritation.

Personal health should be of concern in anything a lifeguard does in or around a beach or pool. For health and sanitary reasons, uniforms and other wearing or drying apparel should be kept clean and borrowing or using someone else's equipment should be avoided.

Clowning or horseplay that results in personal injury while on or off duty certainly shows lack of maturity and is not a good example for patrons.

It is important for the lifeguard to maintain a high degree of physical fitness if he is to respond to emergencies effectively. All guards should swim at least 220 yards every day and a half-mile once a week. The time should be kept and a decrease expected as the season progresses. Use of equipment can be expeditious in rescue work only if constant practice is exercised. Guards should practice at least twice a week with the equipment normally used for rescue purposes at the beach or pool.

In-Service Training

The lifeguard must also maintain a high degree of mental readiness. He must be prepared to act at once and instinctively. This degree of readiness can best be maintained by continuous in-service training. Vivid and intelligent portrayals of ill-handled tragedies with careful, exhaustive analysis of situations and consequences will arouse an awareness of the need to be alert, vigilant and, above all, constant.

Doctors called in to lecture lifeguards on cerebral palsy, epilepsy, asthma, diabetes and cardiac conditions will serve to sharpen minds and, thus, prevent accidents. Knowing what to look for makes an observer more intelligent. The ordinary weaknesses of people without extraordinary physical handicaps, at the beginning of the season when they think they can perform long or fast swims on a par with their feats at the end of the previous season, should be explained by saying they are like recuperants walking again after being bedridden five days. Muscle tone comes back slowly. Harsh exercise in the water without a gradual build-up in the early part of the season will cause nausea, cramps, heart attacks and drownings.

His attitude toward bathers and swimmers in bringing about co-operation has much to do with the success or failure of a lifeguard in handling his assignment. He must be favorably impressive without being offensive. Forearmed as to what good conduct should be and nipping prospective trouble in the bud by a quick but firm objective approach without anger or challenge will avert embarrassment, accidents and riots. Acquainting guards with the position taken by management on the use of supporting devices, snorkels, face masks, swim fins and scuba equipment is necessary. Management must, in advance, through news media, make known to the public its policies on the beach or pool.

Review of communications among guards, between guards and management, between the swimming facility and the doctor or the police is a matter of first order. Seconds save lives.

Should any guard become ill, it is imperative that he notify his supervisor so the post is covered. An appreciation of the moral responsibility borne by a lifeguard comes from the grim, stark horror of witnessing an hysterical mother cringing before the sight of a limp child brought out of the water to her too late because of a misunderstanding of who was on duty.

Competitive meets among lifeguards provide a colorful public spectacle and make drills more interesting and meaningful. There's nothing like a big public show to arouse personal pride and the desire to excel. Five events are suggested for use in pools and three for open beaches:

Event #1—retrieving race: dive, swim twenty yards, surface dive in water at least eight feet deep, recover object (rubber diving brick) from bottom, place on hip, swim to wall, place brick on wall and swim to starting point at opposite end of pool. First one to return to starting point wins.

Event #2—front surface approach and cross-chest tow race: jump into deep water (head must remain above surface), swim twenty yards, do correct front surface approach (including reverse), take no more than three strokes to level victim, go into cross-chest tow and return to starting position. First one to return to starting point wins.

Event #3—rear approach and head tow race: jump into deep water (head must remain above surface), swim twenty yards, do correct rear approach (including reverse), take no more than three strokes to level victim, go into head tow and return to starting position. First one to return to starting point wins.

Event #4—underwater approach and hair tow race: jump into deep water (head must remain above surface), swim twenty yards, do correct underwater approach, bring victim to surface, take no more than three strokes to level victim, go into hair tow and return to starting position. First one to return to starting point wins.

Event #5—tired swimmer's tow race: jump into deep water (head must remain above surface), swim twenty yards, go into tired swimmer's tow, turn victim around and return to starting position. First one to return to starting point wins.

The following events could be adapted for lake or ocean beaches where equipment is normally used for rescue work.

Event #1—buoy rescue: run from guard position on beach (up to 100 yards) into water and swim 100 yards to victim, effect rescue and tow victim back to beach. This could be modified by using a tag line to pull victim and rescuer back. Another interesting variation would have two victims rescued by one guard.

Event #2: boat race from beached position around a buoy one-quarter to one mile offshore and return to beach or straight rowing race from buoy to buoy.

Event #3: simulated rescue of submerged non-breathing victim twenty-five yards offshore with return to shore, transportation to high ground and application of artificial respiration and supplementary care, possibly including inhalator or respirator.

Other purposeful, in-service activities which can help maintain a degree of "sharpness" include water wrestling and "the gauntlet." Water wrestling is best conducted in a restricted deep-water area. The participants may grasp any free, surfaced individual. Blocks, parries and releases are utilized to maintain or obtain a free position. Regrasping the same individual is not permitted. In swimming "the gauntlet," one person at a time is exposed to the unexpected grasping by another as he swims between two parallel lines. Only one person may grasp the swimmer at a time. This may be done by anyone in the line, on the right or left side of the swimmer. After the swimmer has released the hold he takes a place at the end of a line. A swimmer at the head of the line then takes his turn through the gauntlet. This procedure is repeated until everyone in both lines has taken a turn. There are no restrictions as to how or what parts of the swimmer's body may be grasped.

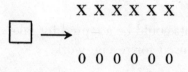

In both these activities, prearranged safety releases ("let go" signals) are advocated.

Public Relations

There certainly can be no doubt that good public relations make for a more pleasant, wholesome and satisfactory employee environment. The question is, how can we accomplish this relationship?

The first important step is to establish the idea of service to the community. Through making the public aware of the service a lifeguard renders, and the arduous training he must undergo to qualify, a greater respect results commensurate with prestige. When this is accomplished, the lifeguard's job becomes easier. However, unless the lifeguard conducts himself in a gentlemanly manner, treats the public with respect, gently but firmly enforces the rules and regulations and indicates his proficiency in his daily performances, his public-relations rating will be poor. The lifeguard's very bearing will have much to do with his success in this regard.

Some general instructions to lifeguards will help materially in getting the public on "their side."

1. Personal appearance should be above reproach at all times. This means being clean-shaven and in spotless uniform.

2. Idling, gossiping, mingling and reading while on duty should be religiously avoided. The public can have nothing but disrespect for the lifeguard under these circumstances, to say nothing of disastrous consequences which may result from lack of alertness or attention to duty.

3. Courteous treatment of patrons is required at all times. Shouting directions or arguing is very undesirable.

4. Any questions directed to the lifeguard which cannot be immediately answered should be courteously referred to a superior.

5. Drinking of intoxicating liquors while on duty or reporting in an intoxicated condition is cause for immediate suspension. What respect can the public possibly have for a lifeguard who even remotely appears to be in such condition?

6. The lifeguard certainly should not abuse the authority given him. He should reflect credit on his organization at all times.

7. Nothing can impress the public more than lifeguards working as a smoothly operating team. If the lifeguard works as a member of such a team, he won't have to look for glory or credit; it will be there.

8. The lifeguard who is thoroughly familiar with the area for which he is responsible, further serves the public in that he can protect his patrons from its hazards.

9. In conclusion, just good, plain, ordinary common sense and common courtesy will go a long way in accomplishing the mission of the lifeguard and make his duty pleasant, satisfying and rewarding.

3

PREVENTIVE LIFEGUARDING

"Preventive lifeguarding" is the term applied to a technique that prevents an accident by eliminating or minimizing the hazard or hazardous behavior. Since an accident in a swimming or boating area could result in serious consequences, it is imperative that all lifeguards develop the technique of preventive lifeguarding.

Accidents are caused by factors in the environment. A slippery deck, water too shallow for diving, a sudden step-off into deep water, horseplay, an unsafe act by an individual such as attempting to swim too far underwater—all these and many others must be recognized by the lifeguard as hazards or hazardous practices if the accident is to be prevented.

Some beach and pool operators have charted the danger areas in their facilities as well as the hazardous practices of their patrons. The Los Angeles Recreation and Parks Department, Aquatics Division, as a result of more than twenty-five years of experience, points out the following as worthy of special attention by swimming-pool lifeguards.

1. *Bathers' entrance:* a desire to get into the water as quickly as possible leads patrons to run from the bathers' entrance to the pool. This should be checked by the guards at the beginning of the season.

If the bathers' entrance is at the deep end of the pool, guards will have to be especially alert for unsuspecting poor or non-swimmers plunging into water over their heads.

2. *Pool deck:* the prime danger on the deck space surrounding the water area is *running*. Many falls resulting in injuries have occurred as a result of an indiscreet runner, and the runner endangers not only himself but the other patrons. Be firm in enforcing the *no running—walk* rule.

3. *Pool ladders:* the pool ladders should not be used as horizontal or parallel bars; they are usually so slippery that such stunts are extremely hazardous. "Green" swimmers often use the ladders to walk down to the bottom, and are liable to be shoved off and unable to handle themselves in deep water. The ladder should be used only for climbing in and out of the

pool. For maximum safety, the user should always face the ladder. Do not permit diving from the ladders. Be especially alert for horseplay in the region of the ladders.

4. *Shallow diving and shallow water:* be alert for inexperienced swimmers diving into shallow water. Often these swimmers dive into the water at an angle that causes them to hit the bottom. Cut heads, injured hands and fingers as well as severe neck injuries often result from diving into shallow water.

5. *Semi-deep water:* semi-deep water is that part of the pool which lies between the buoyed line and the shallow end. The prime danger is usually limited to small children who, not being able to touch bottom, hold onto the overflow trough (scum gutter) and attempt to circle their way around hand-over-hand. If accidentally pushed or shoved from their hand hold, they are over their depth and consequently in danger.

6. *Deep water:* general deep water, that area within the buoyed line and diving-board end of the pool, is a danger area. There are two major hazardous practices—swimmers going too far underwater and poor swimmers in deep water. Many swimmers use this area for underwater swimming and the danger exists in their losing consciousness while doing so; therefore, it is imperative that the water at all times be clear enough to see the bottom. When the water is exceptionally clear, it may appear shallower than it actually is and mislead patrons who are not familiar with the pool. An excellent procedure, if constantly enforced, is that of requiring patrons to pass an "across and back" test before allowing them deep-water privileges.

7. *Diving towers:* the area around a diving tower can be a dangerous one if not properly supervised. Persons who make a back dive may glide into the wall or may dive into another swimmer. On occasions, swimmers making a forward dive will veer off course, dive to the right or left of the board and strike a swimmer. Caution divers to swim back to the deck by swimming to either side of the board, not directly under it.

8. *Diving boards:* the ladder should be used by all persons wishing to dive from the board, and "side mounting," i.e., climbing onto the diving board from the side, or fulcrum, should not be allowed. Only one person on the board at one time should be permitted, and "double bouncing" discouraged. The "double bouncer" takes up more than his share of time on the board, and takes the chance of injury by falling onto the curb or deck. Do not permit horseplay on the board.

9. *Area in front of diving board:* the areas enclosed by a radius approximately fifteen feet from the end of the diving board and the diving

tower should be watched and swimmers cautioned against the danger of being dived on.

10. *Area opposite diving board:* the areas opposite the diving board and diving towers are dangerous, in that persons diving from the edge of the pool may unwarily float or coast into the diver's way and be dived upon. Warn swimmers in this area to keep heads up.

11. *Guard towers and/or chairs:* the guard towers are for the exclusive use of the lifeguard, who is to be unaccompanied at all times, except the time required to make the change for relief purposes. Care should be taken in climbing the towers, making sure that the rungs are not loose or shaky. Check to see that the tower is securely anchored to permit the guard to dive or jump without toppling it. Towers not in good condition should be reported and not used until repaired. Conversation with patrons while on the tower is not in the best interest of safety and should be discouraged.

12. *Curb troughs:* the overflow troughs, or "scum gutters," may prove dangerous to children playing in shallow water, or attempting to climb out. Their elbows or knees may be caught, and help may be needed to get them out. Usually the trapped joint may be freed by bending to such an angle that it offers little or no resistance. The use of soap to obtain a slippery surface will also be found helpful in freeing the limb.

13. *Bathers lying on deck:* all swimmers lying on the deck of the pool should be at least six feet from the curb at the edge of the pool to allow a passageway for bathers walking around the deck. Accidents will occur when bathers walking around the pool stumble or trip over those lying on the deck or their equipment left in the area.

14. *Fountains:* many pools are equipped with fountains at one end, upon which children may attempt to climb, and from which they may dive. Diving from such a height into two and a half feet of water would prove disastrous. Forbid all persons to climb onto these fountains.

15. *General pool area:* the entire pool layout must be watched for rough play, such as "horse and rider," "ducking," "hanging on the fence," "shoving," "cutting corners," etc.

The question as to whether to permit the use of equipment such as water wings, water balls, inner tubes, diving objects and face plates (masks) in a pool is a difficult one. However, there is a principle involved that could serve as an answer—if the swimmer can use the device in such a way so as not to jeopardize his own safety or the safety of others, he should be permitted to use it.

Surf Swimming

Since swimming or bathing in the surf is quite different from pool bathing, it is doubly important for the lifeguard to be on the alert for accident-causing conditions. Many beach patrols train their guards to prevent accidents by being alert to the following.

1. *Swimming at remote places:* swimming should be permitted only at guarded areas.

2. *Rip tides, run outs and other currents:* guards should learn to recognize dangerous conditions and help all swimmers and bathers from these areas. Warning signs should be posted, in addition to verbal warnings given by the guards.

3. *Swimming close to piers or pilings:* keep all swimmers and bathers away from piers and pilings. In addition to causing dangerous currents, they also have sharp cutting edges and surfaces.

4. *Changing bottom conditions:* often, without prior warning, the condition of the bottom will change so as to endanger poor or non-swimmers. Be on the alert for these changes and post *NO BATHING* signs at these spots.

5. *Swimming too far from shore:* be alert to the person who ventures too far from the beach. Swimmers who want to swim a distance should be encouraged to swim parallel to the shore a reasonable distance offshore.

6. *People who drink on the beach:* watch for those who drink intoxicating beverages on the beach. Encourage them to remain out of the water if they are intoxicated.

7. *Inflated air mattresses:* persons who use these devices are in danger of being carried out to sea or dashed on the beach by a breaking wave. A speeding air mattress propelled through the surf by a breaking wave can also inflict serious injuries to other bathers. The use of these devices should be controlled.

8. *Horseplay on the beach:* while the primary responsibility of the guard is to protect the bather in the water, he is often responsible for the safety of those on the beach. Many lifeguards subscribe to this principle— "Any act which jeopardizes the individual's safety or the safety of others should be discouraged."

9. *Guard stands or towers:* bathers should not be encouraged to talk to guards on the stands. It is important for the guard to give optimum attention to those in the water.

It is realistic to expect that even though a lifeguard does all in his power to prevent an accident, an emergency will occur. It is at this time that a few seconds of advance warning may enable the guard to avoid serious trouble. Therefore, one of the more important aspects of preventive lifeguarding is knowing what to look for. The guard's ability to know the signs of impending trouble in the water, to recognize, even anticipate, "tip-off" actions or behavior of swimmers and non-swimmers, will often eliminate or modify situations that may require an actual rescue attempt.

It has often been said that this characteristic requires a so-called "sixth sense" and is best acquired through experience. This may be true, but to leave such an important attribute to chance would only invite trouble.

There is no question about signs of distress such as:

- a call for help
- excessive thrashing of the arms
- abnormal head-bobbing action
- a facial expression of fear or panic
- complete disregard of or failure to acknowledge a "whistle" or megaphone "call"
- frantic efforts to proceed in one direction but body remains in a stationary position or moves in an opposite direction

The ability to detect and recognize these signs at swimming pools should present no real problem for a competent lifeguard. He will quickly distinguish between the "play and fun" actions and the "real" thing. At outdoor areas, especially the ocean beaches where much greater distances are involved, the availability and use of *binoculars* will prove to be most valuable in observing doubtful swimmers, unusual actions in a group of bathers, possible distress situation of a boat offshore and checking any other objects not clearly visible to the naked eye or unattended floating objects drifting or being washed ashore.

Normally, the guard will keep his eyes moving, constantly watching the bathers and swimmers in his assigned area. Look for the unusual; expect the unexpected; anticipate danger. If in doubt, get going; don't wait for a call for help. An occasional glance into the adjacent guard's area often helps detect impending trouble right under his feet, and below his vision or attention when his stand or chair is placed at the water's edge.

"Where shall I focus my attention?" is a common question asked by inexperienced surf beach guards. The Atlantic City Beach Patrol Chief, Richard W. Hughes, has shared years of experience in providing an answer to this question.

During the early part of the lifeguard training period, the candidates are impressed with the importance of watching the "danger line" for the surf bathers.

This line or area is the distance between the chest-high water bather and the swimmer in deep water. Ninety percent of the guard's attention should be devoted to the bathers in this area.

Under normal conditions, the shallow-water bathers, those inside the "danger line," require only ten percent of the guard's attention. Should holes, step-offs, or changing surf conditions warrant, a "tighter" observation must be maintained. Whether it be at a pool, lake or beach, children should always be kept under close observation. Many can swim just well enough to get into trouble. Nearby adult bathers frequently detect or sense that a child is in danger, but lifeguards should not depend on or count on being alerted by them.

Experience has also verified the fact that many people look like "champs" in pool and calm lake water but like "chumps" in surf water. It is important, therefore, that the guards watch the actions of bathers in their areas to determine their familiarity with surf bathing. Just the manner in which they enter the water and get knocked down time and again by the waves is an obvious tip-off.

Chief Hughes also impresses the guards with the fact that in most serious cases they have about an average of three minutes to effect a rescue.

Should any holes, gullies, sloughs, off-sets or rougher surf develop, preventive lifeguarding involves a restriction or relocation of the permitted bathing area and a movement of the flags and/or signs indicating the new limits. It may also be necessary to move the lifeguard stands to more advantageous locations. "Whistling and waving in" all bathers into waist-deep water is another good preventive measure.

If the use of flotation devices (inner tubes, air mattresses, etc.) is permitted at a beach, the guards should always be alert. Offland breezes can easily blow these farther away from shore. If surfboards are permitted, an area well away from bathers should be designated for this purpose. Similar precautions should also prevail with skin and scuba divers, spear fishing, surf casting.

In surf rescue work a guard's ability to hold his breath for at least one minute is essential should he be taken under by the victim, be pounded under by the surf or find it necessary to take the victim under to release a hold. The turbulence and "up-setting" action of a heavy surf often requires some deviation or adaptation of the "standard" methods for releasing holds.

Even though all these aspects of preventive lifeguarding can be read by lifeguards or presented and discussed by the instructor conducting the lifeguard training course, thereby starting the development of a "sixth sense," there is no real substitute for experience. The learning process can also be hastened and made more effective if all newly trained guards are assigned to, or stationed with, a more seasoned, experienced guard. While on duty together, the "veteran" can continue the instruction by pointing out and calling attention to situations and conditions spotted quickly by the trained eye. A good guard will always be aware of local weather conditions and what effect they will have on the safety of bathers. At outdoor areas, the trained eye will also recognize signs of impending bad weather. All persons should be cleared from swimming areas and open beaches during thunderstorms. A few of the more simple cloud formations and their meaning are:

> *Cumulo-Nimbus*—dark and vertical
> —signifies a storm
> *Strato-Cumulus*—continuous, connected globes
> —seen before or after a storm
> *Alto-Cumulus*—high, fleecy, white
> —signifies a storm if they grow large and dark
> —a gray line on the horizon indicates a squall on the way

It has often been said that the best experience comes from making mistakes. This, definitely, should not apply to lifeguards. Their knowledge, skill and judgment is directly related to an environment, the water, in which every bather and swimmer is a potential drowning victim. Nothing should be left to chance or second-guessing when it comes to preventive lifeguarding and actual rescues. When lives are at stake, there is no room for mistakes.

SECTION II

OPERATIONS

4

WATER CONDITIONS

Although "water conditions" in a swimming pool are primarily related to the health of the bathers and swimmers, water conditions in large outdoor bodies of water such as lakes, rivers and tidal waters, especially the ocean, are more directly related to the safety of the bather. Such waters should also be tested and declared suitable for bathing by a local, county or state Department of Health. The greatest danger, of course, is pollution.

In a well-operated pool, the water condition varies very little and rarely brings forth any unusual problem for a lifeguard.

Surf Beaches

By contrast, however, water conditions at outdoor areas mentioned are constantly changing. It is essential for guards on surf beaches to be aware of these conditions and the effect these changes can have on the bathers.

Unfortunately, the terminology used to identify ocean water conditions varies in different parts of the country. However, in the interest of an adequate understanding, the following terms and descriptions are used:

Waves: the one factor that makes a surf beach different from any other beach is the action of the waves. The action of the waves makes or influences all the currents and other conditions that we associate with the surf beach. No two waves are alike; yet they all have certain characteristics in common. They have height from trough to crest, and length from crest to crest. The period is the time it takes for each succeeding crest to pass a fixed point. These characteristics are mainly influenced by the wind and bottom contours. The water that makes up a wave does not move forward with it across the sea. Each particle of water moves in an elliptical pattern, up, forward, down and back to very near its starting point as the wave system moves through the water, much like a sound wave moving through the air.

A wave is born of wind and water. The size is determined by the length of "fetch." The fetch is the distance that the surface water is pushed by the drive of the wind in the same direction and force without obstruction. The longer the fetch, the larger the wave. The largest waves, twenty-five feet or better from trough to crest, are made by gale force winds (forty-five miles per hour or more) blowing over the open sea for days at a time. Large waves travel great distances, many of them over five thousand miles, to come crashing on our shores. The average wave moves through the water at ten to twenty miles per hour. There may be more than one wave system moving through the same water at the same time in different directions, caused by storms or winds in various parts of the sea, far away or in the immediate area. Occasionally waves are caused by underwater earthquakes. Destructive tidal waves are of this type.

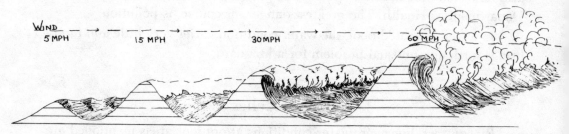

FIG. 1. FETCH—The size, speed and strength of a wave are determined by distance and length of time the wind blows over the open ocean at a given speed

Types of waves: there are many types of waves. A knowledge of them will help in understanding the surf.

a) *Rolling waves:* the rolling wave is the wave of deep water. Started by winds of the open sea hundreds or even thousands of miles away, it comes rolling smoothly through the water like a small moving green hill, up to fifteen feet or more in height. There is no white water or foam, just a solid mound of water traveling at speeds of ten to twenty miles per hour. It moves easily through the water until meeting an obstruction; then it can turn into a vicious, surging, hammering monster or a gentle flow of water, depending on its size, speed and the bottom contours.

b) *Breaking waves:* as the rolling waves near the shore or shallow water, two things happen. The lower part of the wave is held back by friction of the bottom and the wave is pushed higher by the wedging action of the bottom. These two actions cause the top of the wave to peak up and lean forward. The wave becomes steeper and steeper, until finally the topmost part falls over in front of itself and the wave breaks. The broken white water, full of air bubbles, rolls down the front of the main part of the wave and is carried forward by it. The wave continues to break, adding more white water, which is carried forward until it either washes up on the beach or the wave moves into deeper water and assumes its normal shape again. The water just under the white water is this type of wave and is calm and easy to swim in.

c) *Curling waves:* these dangerous waves are called by various names, such as umbrella waves, boomers, grey beards, hollow waves, etc. They are fast, large moving waves, which peak up very high because of their velocity over a rapidly shoaling bottom when they break. They curl 'way over so that the water falls in front of the main part of the wave instead of rolling down. Air is trapped inside the hollow face and forced down by the tremendous weight of falling water. There is a great boiling turbulence which goes deep into the water in front of the wave. This most dangerous type of wave is caused when a fast-moving wave hits a steeply inclined bottom. The lower part of the wave is slowed very quickly by friction with the bottom, and the top continues to move, causing it to peak up high and break in this curling manner. Sometimes the local wind can cause this type of wave; when it blows strongly enough directly against the movement of the wave, it will hold the top from breaking while the wave continues to build up. Finally, the top of the wave crashes over, the spray flying hundreds of feet, very beautiful but dangerous.

These waves are dangerous for three reasons: If a person or a boat is hit by the falling water, it can break the back of either, as easily as breaking a match stick. After the wave breaks, there is so much air mixed in with the water that it will not support the weight of a swimmer and no

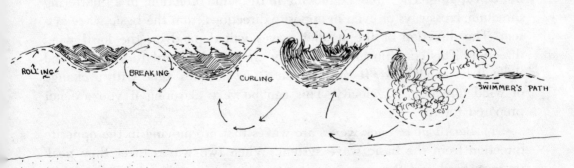

Fig. 2.   Types of Waves Showing Swimmers' Safest and Easiest Path

amount of swimming will bring you to the surface. The turbulence is so great that you actually can't tell up from down; you just have to wait until the air bubbles out of the water and it will support you again. If the water is very shallow a wave of this type could smash a person to the bottom with enough force to cause fractures or unconsciousness.

d) *Capping waves:* whitecaps are caused by local winds of fifteen miles per hour or more. They are simply the water from tops of waves being blown off by the wind. They make the water choppy, which in turn makes swimming or small boat handling difficult. They may be moving with or in a different direction than the larger rolling waves and when coupled with them can make the sea very choppy.

e) *Double waves—cross waves:* double waves are small local waves which are superimposed on the larger basic waves. They might or might

Fig. 3. Cross Waves

not be capping. They may be moving in the same direction, in a quartering direction, crossways or even in opposite directions from the basic wave system. The direction of the smaller waves will depend on the local wind direction. This condition makes a very choppy sea, hard to swim in and difficult for small craft. It can arise in a few minutes' time with a change of wind direction or velocity. This can be very alarming if you are not prepared for it.

f) *Back waves:* back waves are waves that are moving in the opposite direction from the basic wave system. When two waves meet they peak up very hard and the water shoots straight up into the air. This can be very disconcerting and even dangerous to the inexperienced. Back waves are caused in two ways. When the beach is long and very shallow, the breaking waves force a lot of water up on the beach. Sometimes as it flows back down the beach, it will form a wave in the reverse direction, going out to sea instead of coming in. Sometimes when there is a shoal or bar extending from the shore some distance outward, the incoming waves will be bent into a **U** shape around the point until the ends hit together, called a wave of convergence. Occasionally these waves will continue to bend around until they are headed back out to sea. Back waves can also be caused when a wave hits and bounces off a jetty, bulkhead or rocks.

Direction of waves: waves may approach the shore from any angle, depending on the wind direction, or their origin. They may be moving in at right angles to the beach or from an oblique angle to the left or right. It is important to note the direction and force of the waves because they will have a direct influence on the currents and bottom conditions. In some places a wave from one direction will be easy to swim in and the same size wave from another direction will be very difficult to swim in. With diligent study one may even be able to predict the weather by the size, shape, force, speed and the direction of the waves.

The action of the waves around a point of land, rocky headland or a cove will be modified and should be thoroughly studied before you enter the water. It is difficult to tell in advance what the action may be, because of the many local circumstances.

Currents:

    a) *Run back, or undertow:* the run back, or undertow, is caused by the action of gravity on the water that has been washed up on the beach by the waves. The water runs back down the beach, seeking its own level.

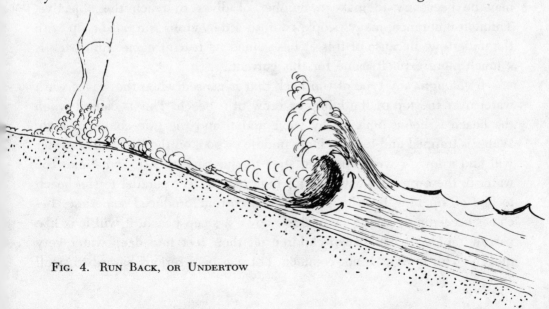

Fig. 4. Run Back, or Undertow

It picks up momentum and keeps moving, to a point about where the waves first started to break, depending on the size of the surf. This current generally runs about twelve to eighteen inches up from the bottom. On short, steep beaches it is very strong; on long, gently sloping beaches, very light. It is confined to the few feet near shore where the water washes up and down the beach. It is intermittent, being absent when the wave is rushing up the beach.

Run back, or undertow, is a much overrated danger, but in a heavy surf it can be dangerous because it will tend to pull a person's feet out toward deeper water and make it difficult to move toward shore. A strong undertow–run back can dig the sand out from underneath the feet or even knock a person's feet right out from under them and leave them rolling in the surf.

The dangers are easy to avoid in deeper water by simply assuming a prone swimming or floating position. With the swimmer's help the waves will then tend to push the body toward shore. A non-swimmer can work himself out of a strong undertow–run back by moving forward with the waves as they rush past, using the hands as paddles. Keep a firm footing between waves so as not to be pulled into deeper water. Be slow and deliberate. Do not start to thrash the arms and legs.

The undertow–run back can be useful to a person who understands it. When there is a heavy surf breaking which would be extremely difficult to swim through, the experienced surf swimmer will surface dive down to the bottom into the run back and be carried into the circular flow of water in the wave. The swimmer will then be carried by the water flow out past the breaking waves with ease. If the surf is breaking for a long distance, it may be necessary to make a number of dives to reach the objective. Through ignorance, many people confuse a dangerous run out or rip with the undertow. Because of this, it has gained its fearful name. Run back is a much more explicit name for this current.

b) *Slough:* any type of run back that is caused when the waves wash water over the top of the hump or brow of a beach. This is caused when the beach is being built up by wave action and the tide comes in high. Water is trapped and forms a large puddle or pool on the beach. The water will find a low or weak spot and start to run back to sea. Sometimes the water in these puddles will flow for hundreds of feet parallel to the beach to find an opening back to the sea. The current produced sometimes becomes exceedingly strong. As it flows down a steep beach, it will look like narrow rapids. It can sweep children off their feet into deep water very quickly. This current is not common, but can be a serious hazard to small fry. It is very similar to a run out or rip of deeper water. Sometimes it will produce its own rip and become a very dangerous situation.

c) *Run out (sea puss) or rip:* this curent is known by many names in different parts of the country. Besides those mentioned above are: run, rip tides, rip current, slough, offshore current, lateral and many others.

Actually there are two types of currents that come in this category. Both are caused by the formation of the bottom, the action of waves and the fundamental law of nature that water always seeks its own level. One is caused by underwater formations roughly parallel to the shore line and the other by formations which are more or less perpendicular to the shore line.

Run out: first we will consider the run out, or sea puss, more common on the east coast of the United States. It is a strong, rather narrow current running out to sea. It is caused by the action of waves over a sand bar or reef that is more or less parallel to the beach. The waves push water over the sand bar until the water level is slightly higher inside the bar than outside, the bar acting as a sort of dam. When this occurs, the water will find a weak or low spot in the bar and start to run back to the open sea.

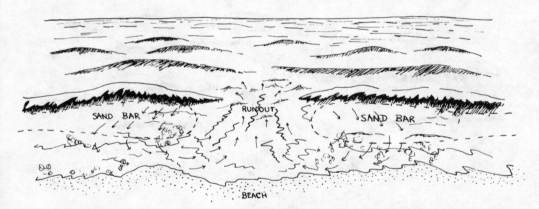

Fig. 5. Run Out, or Sea Puss

As more and more water is pushed over the bar by the waves, the run out will become stronger and bigger, scouring a large hole in the bar. This out-going current can become very strong, up to five or six miles per hour, depending on how much water is coming over the bar. It will be very weak near shore. It will pick up speed and strength as it nears the hole in the bar and be at its strongest as it passes through the bar. It soon loses itself in the open sea. The run out may be any size in width from a few yards across to fifty yards or more. It may be running straight out to sea or it may curve up or down the beach, depending on the wind, the tide, the set or drift, the contour of the bottom and many other variables. The run out generally flows steadily for some time but may start or stop very suddenly, mostly depending on the tide and wind. It may vary in length from 100 yards or so to over one-half mile or more, depending on the distance from shore or the bars or reefs.

Rip: the rip, or offshore current, more common to the west coast of the country, is mostly caused by irregularities of the ocean floor which are more or less perpendicular to the shore line. As an even wave crest approaches the shore, even a very slight irregularity of the bottom will bend the crest. This is known as wave convergence. If there is a ridge on the bottom, the wave will be held back and become concave in shape as it nears shore. If there is a hole or valley, the crest will speed up and become convex. The concave wave caused by a ridge or shoal will converge the wave energy, making the wave higher and stronger, whereas the effect of a hole is to disperse the energy and height of the wave.

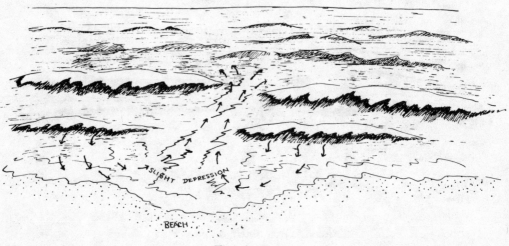

Fig. 6. Rip

The shoreward movement of water is intensified over a shoal because of the contingence of waves which build up water to a greater height shoreward of these shoals or ridges. As the wave breaks on the beach, it flows to either side of the ridge and then back to the sea. If there are a series of these ridges, the flow of water off them and back into deeper water between them will make a strong but intermittent rip. Near shore, large waves will break up the rip temporarily. The rip will be more steady outside the surf line. The larger the surf, the stronger the rip. If the waves are three feet or less in height, the currents are generally so weak that they can be disregarded. When the waves are over four feet, the currents can become troublesome.

A hole or valley perpendicular to the beach will have the same effect by drawing water in from shallower areas on either side.

In conjunction with rips caused by holes or ridges, the along-shore, drift or set current may be diverted offshore by the rip or ridges and so add its force.

The run out or rip can be identified by a number of signs. Look for: a place on the bar or reef where the waves do not break, a section of water that looks different from the surrounding water, little waves that seem to jump up and down, dirty or darker water, a streak of foam or flotsam moving seaward. At low tide, the gaps in the bar or reef can sometimes be plainly seen. A beach with ridges will indicate the probability of rips. Seen from the air, the fan-shaped area of discolored water opening out from a narrow neck near shore is typical of a rip.

These are the most dangerous ocean currents as far as bathers are concerned. To a person who does not know the beach, the smoother water and the lighter surf of the run out or rip are inviting places to swim or bathe. Persons caught in it find themselves being carried rapidly away from shore and safety. They soon become exhausted and panic-stricken when they find it impossible to make headway against the current. Often, more than one person is involved. Would-be rescuers get into difficulty trying to help, and the lifeguard becomes faced with a very difficult rescue operation.

If caught in a strong run out or rip, the simplest way out of it is to swim parallel to the shore across the current. Do not buck it. It will be easier if you swim in the general direction of the waves, the wind or set. Once out of the strong current, it will be easy to swim ashore. A swimmer or lifeguard should be careful not to be caught in the feeder currents as he approaches shore and be swept back into the rip.

The rip can be very useful to a lifeguard, if he understands its action. By swimming in it, he can quickly move out through a very heavy surf. It is easier to take a surfboat or board out through the rip.

d) *Set:* set, drift, along-shore current or shore current is a current of water that moves parallel to the beach. It is caused by wind and wave action. When the wind blows at other than right angles to the beach, it will start the surface water moving in the same direction. It will also make the waves come in at an angle to the beach. This combined action of surface water and waves will induce a current to run parallel to the beach in the general direction of the wind. This current can also be produced by a heavy surf breaking on the beach at an angle even with an opposing wind. The set current can become very strong, up to four miles per hour. Generally, it is apparent only on the shore side of the bar or reef and close to shore.

The set current can be dangerous because it will carry bathers away from the protected area into danger zones such as run outs, rips, jetties, rocks and other obstructions. A lifeguard, when making a rescue, must

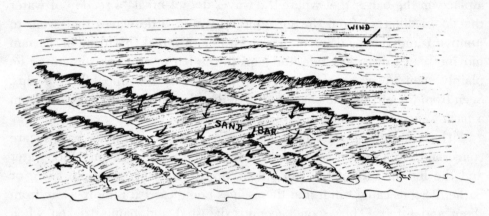

FIG. 7. SET, DRIFT OR SHORE CURRENT

take it into consideration when making his entry into the water, so as not to be carried away from his victim.

A swimmer should maintain his position by constantly referring to a fixed landmark on shore. A good rule is always to swim or walk into the current.

An obstruction on the bottom such as a ridge or valley, a groin, jetty, pier, rock formation or wreck may divert the current to flow seaward instead of along the shore, thus changing it into a very dangerous run out or rip.

e) *Step-off, or hole:* another hazard which is due to the action of run back is the step-off, or hole. Sometimes the sand, loose gravel and bits of shells carried by the run back will build a ledge, deposited when the current slows and stops. In effect, this makes a sudden stepdown, or hole six to eighteen inches. The edge of this step is very loose and soft. It can be dangerous for two reasons. A youngster stepping into the hole may go from waist deep to water over his head; a large person may be thrown off balance and be upset by a wave. A lifeguard running into the surf looks very silly when suddenly he falls flat as he steps into a hole.

f) *Pot Holes:* occasionally, the currents on a surf beach will dig holes of various sizes and depth in irregular patterns on the bottom. The edges may be sharply defined or very gradual. At this time, there doesn't seem to be much knowledge of how or why these pot holes occur except that they are generally in the vicinity of strong conflicting currents. The obvious danger is of people stepping into them over their heads and of possibly being swept out to sea by one of the currents.

Tides: the tides are caused by the gravitational pull of the moon and the sun. In most places, the tide changes from high to low twice a day. The difference in water depth may range from a few inches to forty or fifty feet, but the average difference between high and low tide in the United States is about four feet. The highest and lowest tides each month are during the full moon and the new moon, when the sun, the moon and the earth are in line. In many places, the wind will also have some effect on the tides. An onshore wind will increase the height of a tide; the offshore wind, lessen it. The time of the tides advances about fifty minutes each day. Tide tables are published locally and should be referred to frequently.

There are two important things to be aware of concerning tides. The changing depth of water which exposes or conceals the bottom and changes safe wading areas to deep pools is a constant hazard, especially around bars, reefs and other obstructions. The influence of the tides on all the other currents and waves is very great. It can cause them to start, stop, change direction, size or strength. A beach that is quite safe for swimming at one

FIG. 8. EFFECT OF TIDE ON SAND BAR AND BEACH

phase of the tide can become very hazardous during another phase. Local observation is most important in determining the exact effect of the tides for any one locality, particularly on the currents around jetties, coves, inlets, bars, reefs or other obstructions. An awareness of the tides and changing conditions is of a great importance to the swimmer and lifeguard.

Bars and Reefs: a bar is a mound of sand that is built up by wave action somewhat off shore. Generally, they will run more or less parallel to the beach, but in some places they may run in any direction and be any shape. There may be a number of bars, one after another, particularly around inlets. Bars, being made of sand, have treacherous ways of changing. They appear, disappear, change size or position constantly and are, therefore, completely unpredictable from day to day.

A reef is made up of rock or the hard lime shells of the coral animals. The reef is generally a narrow ridge which runs mostly parallel to the beach. It grows or is worn away so slowly that it can be considered an unchanging feature of the beach. The deeper water between the bar or reef and shore is known as a channel, slough or hole.

The bar or reef presents three dangers to the bather or swimmer. One or more of the dangerous currents is to be expected and is the foremost danger to swimmers. These currents can sweep a swimmer beyond, around or on the bar or reef. The pounding of the surf on a reef can literally batter a person to death. Another problem is caused by the tides. At low tide, the bar or reef could be dry or have only a few inches of water on it; the channel which separates it from shore, only two or three feet of water. As the tide comes in, the water depth could change to three feet on the bar and six or seven feet in the channel, trapping poor or non-swimmers on the bar. This danger should be closely watched by lifeguards.

Wind: the wind which starts the waves in motion will have an effect on waves until they finally destroy themselves on the shore. The wave will continue to move through its water, even though the original wind which produced the wave was thousands of miles away and may have blown itself out many hours or days ago. The local winds will continue to modify the surf conditions. A moderate or strong sea breeze or onshore wind (from the water toward land) will make the surf heavy and rough. A land breeze or offshore wind (blowing from land toward water) will make a smooth, even surf, and tend to make the waves smaller. If there is a heavy surf rolling in and a strong land wind, the waves will peak up very high; the wind will blow the tops of the waves off into a fine spray for hundreds of feet—a most beautiful sight with the sun putting dancing rainbows all through the spray. However, these waves may become pounding hollow-backs with tremendous destructive power.

A wind coming from a quartering direction off the sea will make a very choppy surf with confused wave patterns.

A wind blowing directly onshore or offshore will generally moderate toward late afternoon or change to a quartering wind. A quartering wind off the water in the morning will generally increase in force all during the day. A quartering wind off the land will moderate and about noon will shift to a quartering wind off the water, and then shift back to a land breeze in the early evening. These are very general observations. A study of the local wind actions is important.

When the wind shifts from one direction to another, increasing or decreasing in velocity, you should look for a change in surf conditions, the set, the run out or rip, the waves and the general patterns of the beach. Occasionally a shift from land to sea breezes will form a dense fog bank in a few minutes' time, making it difficult or impossible for the lifeguard to see the bathers.

Obstructions: most fixed obstructions in the surf such as pilings, wrecks, jetties, groins, rocks and piers present hazards. Around large ones, there will most likely be strong currents of one kind or another to endanger the swimmer. If the obstructions are located in the surf line, the surge of waves can smash a person against them with dire results. Most obstructions that have been in the water for any length of time will have very sharp edges carved on them by the sand and be covered by barnacles, mussels, oysters or coral, all of which have many razor-sharp cutting edges.

Floating debris in the surf is just like a battering ram as it moves with the surge of the waves. Spikes, bolts, barnacles, etc., may add many cutting edges to its crushing power.

It is best to stay away from any obstructions in the surf, if possible. Should you get swept into fixed obstructions, keep your body as limp and relaxed as possible, protect your head and try to work your way off. Do not stiffen your body or thrash about.

Always stay at one end or the other of floating obstructions so that the wave can't push it over you or the run back drag it over you. Stay away from any obstructions if you can, unless approaching them is necessary to save a life.

Swimming Pools

This information will relate to water conditions other than those involving the filtration of swimming-pool water. However, it is believed that a swimming-pool lifeguard should have an understanding and appreciation of this aspect of facility operation and maintenance. If a training course for pool lifeguards only is being conducted and the guard's job responsibility includes the operation of filters, chlorinators, etc., the course should include more specific information and instruction beyond that included in the following outline.

1. *Three of the most common types of swimming pools*

   a) *Fill and draw*
      (1) this type must have a cheap supply of water, since the water is discarded as it becomes contaminated.
      (2) fresh sterile water is used as replacement.

   b) *Flow through*
      (1) water from a moving stream or river is diverted to, and permited to flow through, an enclosed "pool" area.

   c) *Recirculating*
      (1) the most common type of indoor and outdoor pool in operation today.
      (2) the source of water may be from a well or from a reservoir coming into the pool system as "raw" city water.
      (3) the water is constantly re-used.
      (4) the water is pumped from the pool through filters, sterilized and returned to the pool.
      (5) small amounts of new or raw water are added, usually automatically, to compensate for loss of water from splashing into the overflow trough and from some evaporation.

2. *Contamination**

   a) *Visible* contamination is matter such as dust, algae, lint and hair.

   b) *Invisible* matter is microscopic bacteria and germs which are frequently detrimental to health.

---

* All water in indoor and outdoor pools, as well as lake, river and tidal-water areas used for bathing and swimming should be carefully analyzed by the state or municipal department of health or an authorized agent. Most swimming-pool codes specify that the chemical and bacteriological analysis shall be made in accordance with procedures described in the current edition of "Standard Methods for the Examination of Water and Sewage" (published jointly by the American Public Health Association and the American Water Works Association).

3. *Removal*

  a) Visible matter is removed by filters and screens.

  b) Invisible matter is removed by filters and chemical action.

4. *Filters*

  a) The vertical-pressure sand-gravel filter probably outnumbers other types in operation today.

  b) The gravity-type sand filter was the common installation prior to the development of a).

  c) The diatomaceous-earth filter installations have increased during recent years.

The basic characteristics of sand filters are:

- a sealed tank containing various grades of sand through which the water flows
- a fine strainer at the bottom to retain the sand
- an alum "flock" on top of the sand introducing the alum into the main flow of water before it enters the filter
- the alum is fed through an alum pot in metered amounts
- when the "flock" becomes loaded with debris, the flow through the filter is reversed and water involved is discarded. This is called *backwashing*
- the recommended rate of filtration should not be greater than three gallons per minute per square foot of effective filter surface area
- the minimum rate of backwash should not be less than fifteen gallons per minute per square foot of filter area
- the filter should be able to recirculate the pool water completely every eight hours or less

The basic characteristics of diatomaceous-earth filters are:

- the "earth" in the tank accomplishes the filtering action instead of the sand-gravel beds
- if the filter tank is of the open type, the *filtration tubes* must be regularly pre-coated with diatomaceous earth. There are many commercial names, or trade names, for this product
- in both the closed and open systems, the filter aid should be fed continuously into the influent line
- all filter elements should consist of metal alloy or ceramic material resistant to corrosive water

- the maximum rate of filtration should not exceed two gallons per minute per square foot of effective filter area
- a complete recirculation of the pool water should be possible every six to eight hours

5. *Sterilizing*

The sterilizing, disinfecting or purification agent used almost exclusively is *chlorine*. This is usually fed into the main as close to the pool feed lines as possible. Bromine and iodine are also used, and in some opinions they are preferable to chlorine.

Remember: chlorine is the basic chemical in lung-destroying gases. Take every precaution in handling the bulk supply. Two gas masks should be readily available if the agent is chlorine gas. Know how to use this piece of personal, protective safety equipment.

6. *Chlorinators*

a) The dry-feed type meters the gas directly into the main. This type should be periodically checked for leaks, especially along the line from the machine to the main.

b) The liquid-feed type meters the gas into water in a mixing vial within the machine after which the solution is fed into the main.

c) The hypo-chlorinator is a meter-controlled pump device which injects a hand-mixed solution of chlorine directly into the main. Precautions should be taken when mixing the solution (usually calcium chlorine powder containing about seventy percent available chlorine and water).

7. *Chemical quality of water*

Checking or testing the pool water is one of the most common responsibilities of pool lifeguards. The New Jersey Swimming Pool Code requires that this be done not less than four times during any day the pool is in operation. Regular forms for recording these "readings" should be available and are frequently provided by the municipal board of health.

The chlorine which has been injected into the system by one of the previously described devices remains in the water until completely used. This is called the *residual*. In testing pool water for the free chlorine residual, 1 cubic centimeter (cc) of *ortho-tolidine* is added to 10 cc of pool water in a tube. After a slight agitation of this solution, the resultant color (usually amber) is compared to a set of standard colors in a device called a comparator. A marginal chlorination would be from 0.4 to 0.6 or 0.7 parts per million (ppm), with a pH of 7.3–7.8. A high free residual chlorination would be 1.0 to 2.0 ppm with a pH of 8.2–8.6.

In testing pool water for acidity or alkalinity, pH is the identifying symbol. To 10 cc of pool water in a tube, 1 cc of *phenol red* is added. After agitation, the resultant color is compared to a set of standard colors scaled with readings ranging from 6.0 to 8.4. A good reading would be within 7.0 to 7.6 range.

Note: There are many types of testing equipment (comparators) available for purchase from commercial chemical firms and swimming-pool-equipment supply companies.

The chemical which is added to pool water in respect to the pH is *soda ash.* This is usually added immediately after backwashing the filters in a quantity which will result in a pH reading of 8.2.

Another chemical commonly associated with pool operation is *copper sulphate* (Cu SO4). This is added directly to the pool in an approximate quantity of three pounds per million gallons of water. This chemical will kill any algae that grow in the water. It should be added at the end of a day or before an idle period. Do not use when bathers are in the water.

8. *Physical quality of water*

When in use, the water of a pool should be clear enough to permit a black disk six inches in diameter, placed on the bottom at the greatest pool depth, to be clearly visible from the pool deck at all distances up to ten yards.

9. *Floating debris and sediment*

The equipment used at pools for the removal of floating debris is a "skimmer," a piece of wire netting, screen or cheesecloth fastened to a small frame at the end of a long pole. For the usual-size indoor pool, a pole one foot longer than half the pool width is adequate. This equipment is also available from commercial firms.

The removal of sediment from pool water can be accomplished by brushing it to the effluent line, where it will be carried to the filters. This task is frequently part of a lifeguard's job at large outdoor pools. By the end of a season many guards have become familiar with shallow-water diving helmets or weighted vests and masks with attached air hoses, and have become quite adept at pushing a broom along the bottom.

A more satisfactory and efficient method involves a vacuum cleaner. Those which combine a brush and suction are preferred. This equipment is more practical at the smaller indoor pools, where the job can be done by one man, rather than at the larger outdoor pools, where much longer lengths of vacuum hose and at least two men would be required. A regular schedule for this pool-maintenance job should allow adequate time to vacuum the entire bottom and side walls during one hook-up of the equipment. The best time is before the pool is opened for the day. Much of the sediment has had ample time to settle during the preceding night.

There are many other important aspects of this subject, but it is not the intent of the Manual to present a more detailed explanation of equipment and procedures bearing on swimming-pool water conditions.

Bathing Beaches, Ponds, Lakes and Rivers

When resorting to swimming rescues and assists without equipment at large inland beaches, there are other factors and situations that must be considered. For example, at beaches on the Great Lakes, it is necessary after every storm to take soundings of the swimming area, because bottom conditions and water depths are usually affected by the movement of the waves and currents. This is especially true where jetties are located, as water may be ten feet deep before a storm and only three feet after the storm. Prevention of bathers' getting into hazardous areas is important and depth markers should be placed as warnings. This will also facilitate any swimming rescue that might be necessary because the lifeguard will know in advance what the bottom conditions are and the depths of the water within the swimming area. In many cases, it will only be perhaps two or three feet deep. This can change considerably after a storm and cause a different plan of operation in swimming rescues to be put into effect. In many cases of swimming assists, the lifeguard may take the person in trouble to the nearest shallow-water area, where they can both be transferred to a boat for returning to shore. It is therefore imperative that water depths be marked daily in order that a lifeguard know where the various shallow-water areas are in relation to deeper areas. Many times a lifeguard will not be present when depth markers are posted and will therefore have to rely on the locations being accurately marked each day. These markers will also serve as a warning to swimmers when depth changes occur.

At smaller lakes and streams where there are beaches, the problem is not as great, because relatively small bottom changes occur in these situations. Occasionally in streams, there may be bottom changes or debris following a period of high water and fast current. It will be necessary for the lifeguard force to explore the bottom completely, then remark the swimming area and any new hazards that have developed which cannot be minimized or removed.

Swimming rescues will not always be made under ideal conditions such as flat water, no wind, no current, etc. Under ideal conditions, a swimming rescue can generally be accomplished by one person, as he has no forces to combat other than the victim. It will be of special importance to the new or inexperienced lifeguard to become acquainted with the various currents and water conditions that can develop as the result of wind blowing from different points of the compass. On the Great Lakes, water conditions are generally affected more by wind than on smaller inland lakes. Wind will create choppy wave conditions as well as currents which can present a real problem to the lifeguard in making his rescue. Each time there is a bottom change brought on by a storm, there will be a change in currents. The strength and amount of current will depend on the wind velocity and direction. Therefore, it will be necessary for the lifeguard to chart currents daily and pay particular attention to any wind changes during the day. Even a well-trained lifeguard in good physical condition can become exhausted if he is trying to perform a swimming rescue in a long shore current and is not using the current to his advantage. The same thing applies to rescues in streams and rivers where there are established beaches. The lifeguard must be aware of the conditions existing each day so that he can determine whether he can perform a rescue single-handed or if he will need assistance.

A table of wind velocities and currents at the beach can be made up for varying wind directions and bottom conditions that are observed as being fairly constant over a period of time. Thus, a lifeguard can consult the table for a specific weather condition and have some idea as to what currents and wave forces he could expect to encounter that day. However, relying on a chart alone would not be recommended over posting a daily check on these conditions so that the lifeguards and beach patrons alike would be alerted as to what to expect.

5

RESCUE EQUIPMENT

Lifeguard, or rescue, equipment for use at indoor and outdoor swimming pools has become fairly well standardized over the years.

Whenever possible and practical, a good lifeguard will always use some type of equipment when making a rescue. In most instances, such action will mean an easier, faster and safer rescue. "Swimming rescues without any equipment, *only* as a last resort" is a good rule to remember. In almost all the long-established, well-organized beach patrols, it is mandatory for the guards to use equipment in all rescue attempts, except perhaps those called wading or shallow-water assists.

There are also situations at swimming pools when good judgment on the part of a guard would result in a rescue attempt without equipment. For example, it might be unwise to throw a ring buoy to a victim if there was a possibility of hitting someone else. It would probably also be better and quicker not to use equipment if a victim is in close proximity to safety, the side of the pool or standing-depth water. In these instances, a simple hand extension or a bottom push would be quite effective.

Many local or state swimming-pool ordinances or codes clearly spell out what the minimums are concerning available rescue or emergency equipment. Most frequently included in such codes are:

Pole or Shepherd's Crook

At most indoor pools the light bamboo pole is a familiar sight. Such a pole should be long enough to extend at least one-half the width of the pool or be from ten to twelve or fifteen feet in length. Although a bamboo pole does not require great strength to handle, a guard should be aware of possible injuries to fingers and hands from splinters or incised wounds if the poles are allowed to be cracked or split. Poles should be kept in good repair with tape wrappings or discarded and replaced. In recent years, the use of

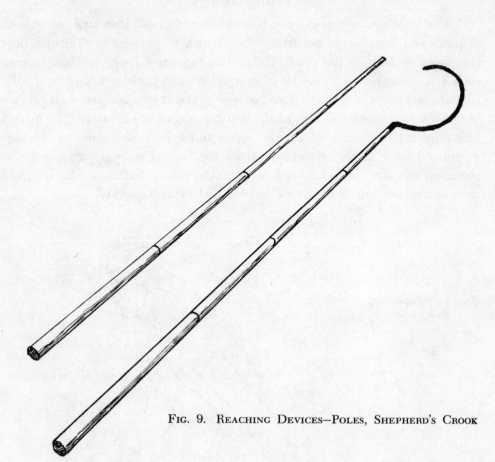

FIG. 9. REACHING DEVICES—POLES, SHEPHERD'S CROOK

light tubular aluminum or telescoping fiber glass poles has eliminated this problem. The pole provides a means of extending the rescuer's reach and should be placed in such a position as to permit the victim to grasp the end.

One of the oldest known pieces of swimming-pool equipment is the shepherd's crook—a long pole with a blunted hook large enough to encircle the victim's body. With it, a person may be grappled and hauled to safety even though unconscious or too weak to hold on. Perhaps the main disadvantage of the crook for many years was its weight. It took an extremely strong person to handle it easily and effectively. More recently, crooks that can be attached to an end of a lightweight aluminum pole have become available.

Ring Buoy

The light casting ring buoy is considered almost standard equipment at pools and beaches where it may be thrown to persons in difficulty near the shore or side of the pool. Today the throwing buoy is about fifteen inches in diameter and may be of canvas-covered cork or kapok or a solid ring-shaped piece of polyethylene, weighing about two and one-half pounds with sixty to seventy-five feet of three-sixteenths or one-quarter-inch manila line attached by means of an eye splice and a four-inch wooden "lemon" or spliced loop at the extreme end of the line. The buoy should be so mounted or coiled on a four-spindle wooden frame that it can be removed with one movement of the arms and readied for use quickly.

FIG. 10. THROWING RING BUOY

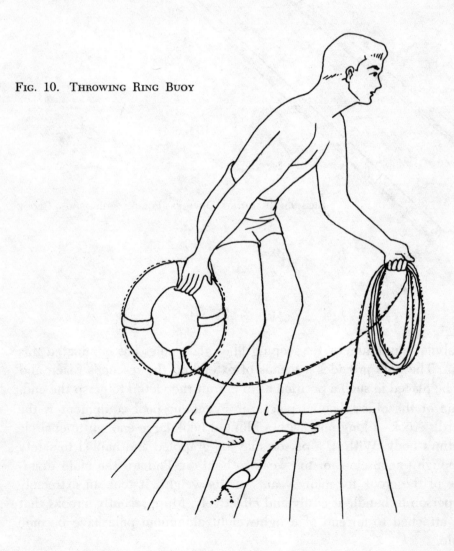

Hand, or Heaving, Line

A less expensive piece of rescue equipment is the hand, or heaving, line, another method of extending a rescuer's reach. Any strong and properly coiled and thrown piece of line can be used to effect a rescue up to distances of fifty feet. Students enrolled in lifesaving courses are familiar with a sixty-foot length of three-eighths- or one-quarter-inch manila with an eye splice on one end and the other end fashioned into a large knot called a "monkey fist." Most lines, because of their light weight, cannot be thrown as far as a ring buoy without a substantial monkey fist.

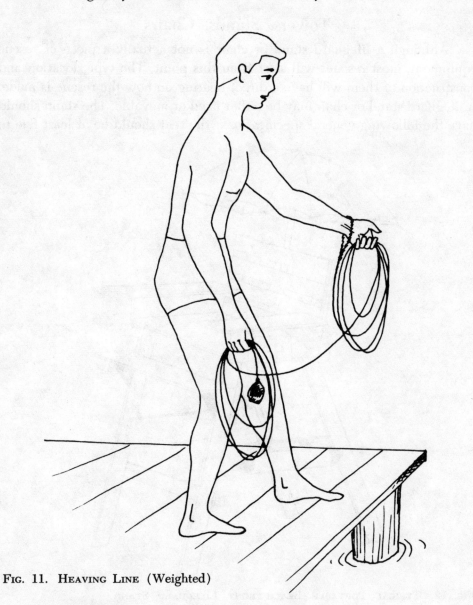

FIG. 11. HEAVING LINE (Weighted)

Emergency Light

Although not essentially related to rescue equipment, the availability of some kind of emergency lighting in the event of power failure at night at an indoor or outdoor pool is recommended. A readily available portable light in such instances would be most valuable to a lifeguard. Few people have ever had the experience of swimming in total darkness. Grave concern and even panic can be prevented by the prompt use of an emergency light and reassuring instructions by the lifeguard.

Towers, Stands, Chairs

Although a lifeguard stand or chair is not actually a piece of rescue equipment, most rescues will start from this point. The type, location and construction of them will have a direct bearing on how the rescue is made. A lifeguard stand or chair may be either fixed or movable. The stand should have the following general specifications: the seat should be at least five to

FIG. 12. TYPICAL PORTABLE BEACH-FRONT LIFEGUARD STAND

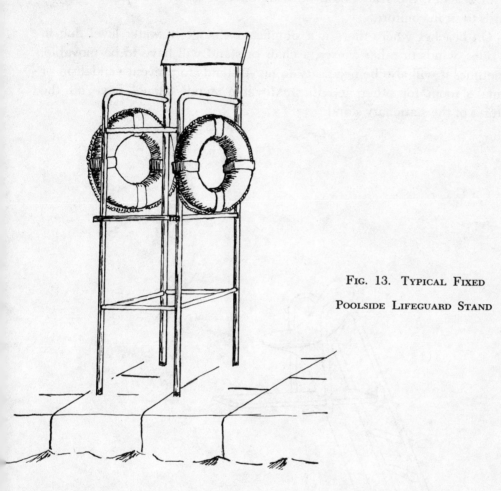

Fig. 13. Typical Fixed
Poolside Lifeguard Stand

six feet above the ground, deck or dock level. It should be comfortable enough for the guard to spend hours at a time in. There should be provisions made for shade and shelter for the guard, either a roof or place for an umbrella. A footrest and backrest are important. A hook, stand or supports for the particular type of rescue equipment to be used should be attached.

If there is no change in water level in the bathing facility, a fixed, permanent structure can be installed. At swimming pools, this is generally made of galvanized, chrome or stainless-steel pipe set into the deck of the pool. Many suitable models are available from pool supply houses. At the pond, lake or river, it is generally a wooden structure built on piling sunk into the beach or bottom. It could also be built on the dock structure.

A shelf or locker for first-aid equipment is also important. A ladder or steps for mounting the stand is advisable. The stand should be strong and stable. On all beaches, the seat should be wide enough for two or possibly three guards to sit in comfort.

On beaches where there is a significant change in water level due to the tides, winds or other causes, a chair or stand will have to be movable. Sometimes it will also be necessary to move stands to prevent vandalism or to make room for other activities. Movable stands should have all the features of the stationary stand.

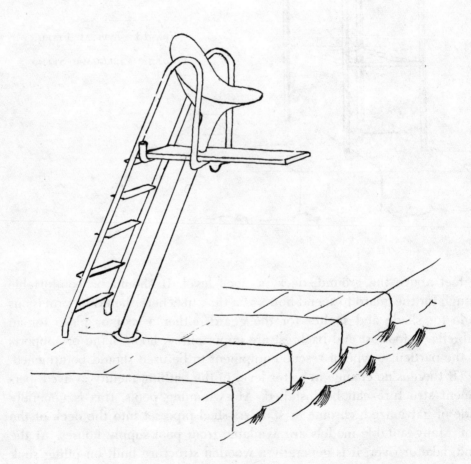

Fig. 14. Contemporary Fixed Poolside Lifeguard Stand

Boats

The rowboat has been the most commonly used water craft throughout the world. Because of its stability, the rowboat is a most valuable and effective craft for lifeguard and rescue work.

Of all the known distinct types and combinations of types, one of the best all-'round boats for lifesaving work is the dory-skiff. Its main features are a sharp overhanging bow, a square stern, slightly flaring sides and a flat bottom.

Fig. 15. Dory—Surface Rescue Boat

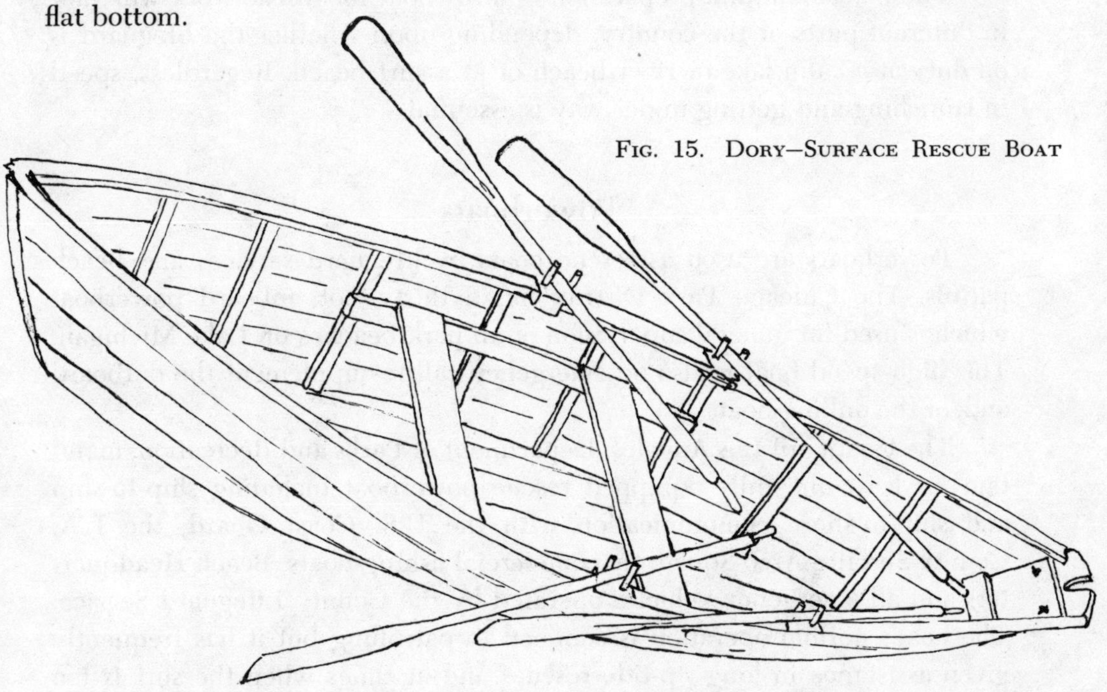

Rowboats made of wood have the advantage of being naturally buoyant, are easily repaired and will provide years of service with ordinary, simple care.

Boats made of metal have increased in popularity. The necessary buoyancy in case of capsize or upset is provided by air tanks or chambers located forward under the bow deck or seat and aft, under the stern seat. In recent years, metal-boat manufacturers have replaced the air tanks with a more dependable means of emergency buoyancy. Blocks of styrofoam or polyethylene are now to be found fastened under the seats in these boats. Boats constructed with synthetic resins such as fiberglass, plastics, etc., have made substantial gains in sales.

In general, a fully equipped boat for lifesaving purposes will have the following: extra oars and rowlocks or thole pins, one or more ring buoys with line attached, a rescue pole, an anchor and line, bailers and a first-aid kit.

All equipment except that needed at the moment should either be lashed to the thwarts or seats (oars and pole) or kept waterproof (first-aid kit) in a suitable container. In some boats, the "cuddy," a waterproof cabinet under the stern thwart, provides this.

In more than one instance, a life line looped from the gunwales on the outside of steamship lifeboats has afforded many swimmers a convenient place to grasp, following disaster at sea.

The placement and preparation of a rowboat for rescue work will vary in different parts of the country, depending upon whether the lifeguard is on duty at a calm lake or river beach or at a surf beach. Regardless, speed in launching and getting under way is essential.

Powerboats

Powerboats are used as rescue boats by lifeguard services and beach patrols. The Chicago Park District has a thirty-foot, inboard powerboat which is used for general supervision of all park beaches on Lake Michigan. This high-speed boat is also on emergency call to supplement the outboard and/or the pulling boats.

The County of Los Angeles, Department of Parks and Recreation, maintains at least one fully equipped rescue powerboat including ship-to-ship and ship-to-shore communication with the U.S. Coast Guard, the L.A. County Sheriff's Areo Squadron, commercial fishing boats, Beach Headquarters and all emergency vehicles operated by the County Lifeguard Service. The boat's normal operation is confined to patrolling but it has frequently given assistance in long rip-tide rescues and at times when the surf is too large or heavy to bring a victim back to the beach. It is not used inside the surf line because the boat is too large and heavy to maneuver.

Rescue Buoys

The importance of using flotation equipment in surf rescues cannot be overemphasized. The waves, tides, rips, run outs and other surf currents make the task of performing a rescue a difficult and exhausting one. When the victim(s) is reached, it most often will be found that he needs support, reassurance and assistance through the surf back to shore. The rescuer himself will often need a place to rest a few minutes. A piece of flotation equipment that will support four or more persons is a necessity on every surf beach.

Most of the major beach patrols of the country have mandatory rules that a lifeguard must take a rescue buoy when a rescue is made, even in shallow water. A good rescue buoy with a trail or beach line to shore is probably the best and most important piece of equipment a surf guard can have.

A rescue buoy should have the following characteristics: it must be buoyant enough to support at least four people with their heads out of water. It must be small enough and light enough to be easily handled and towed by one man. It must be shaped in such a way that it will move easily through the water. It must be rigged so that it will be out of the way when being towed by a swimmer and yet be quickly available. There must be a safe and simple way for the victims to hold onto it. There must be a place to secure a trail line to it, and it must be rugged enough to stand up under the hard usage of the surf for many years. Buoys are made in three general designs and of many materials.

1. *Torpedo buoys:* one of the best pieces of surf rescue apparatus is the torpedo buoy. It is so designed and rigged that it can be taken out through almost any surf; it can be used as a support for several victims and, by means of a line attached to it, the connection with the beach need not be broken if the victim is within range.

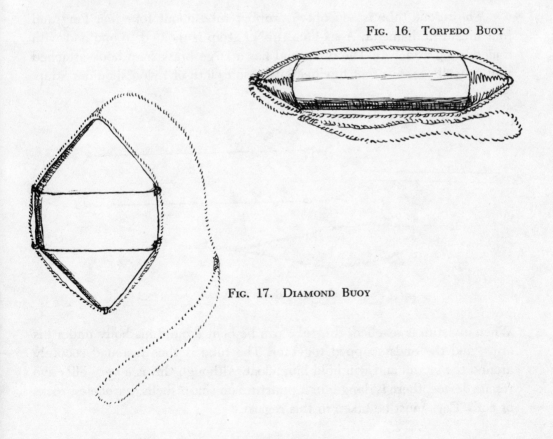

FIG. 16. TORPEDO BUOY

FIG. 17. DIAMOND BUOY

2. *Diamond buoys:* the diamond buoy is a flat, diamond-shaped hollow metal or solid wood buoy eighteen to twenty-four inches long and three to four inches thick. It has the same hand lines around its outer edge as the torpedo buoy and is equipped with a similar towline. It is more stable for the victim to hold onto but more difficult for a lifeguard to tow through rough water.

3. *Rubber buoys:* there is a torpedo type of buoy made of heavy neoprene rubber and inflated with air. These are very good buoys but are subject to cuts or punctures from sharp shells, barnacles, etc. They should be used only on beaches where these hazards do not exist.

Rescue Tube

The rescue tube is a neoprene rubber tube about four feet long and four inches in diameter. A six-inch rubber strap is molded to one end with a metal ring attached. The other end has a large brass snap hook attached to it as well as a five-foot towline with a soft cloth or nylon shoulder strap.

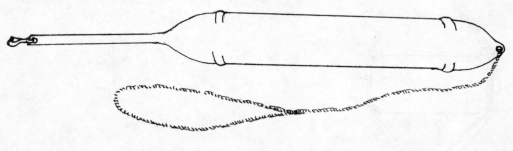

Fig. 18. Rescue Tube

When a victim is reached, this tube can be bent around his body under his arms, and the ends snapped together. The tube is thus fastened securely around the victim and will hold him afloat. Although this is a very effective rescue device, there is danger of a puncture on sharp shells, barnacles, rocks or nails. Care must be taken in this regard.

Lines and Reels

Lines, other than the hand, or heaving, line, have long played an important role in preventing accidents at many bathing areas.

The stretched or buoyed lines in indoor and outdoor pools, separating the shallow and deep water areas, are familiar sights, as are the clearly defined swimming areas at summer-camp water fronts. Swimming areas for various classifications or abilities of the campers are frequently identified by different colored "lemons" or booms which float the line—red for non-swimmers and beginners, white for deep-water swimmers.

Although motorboat operators should know enough to stay out of swimming and bathing areas, the inherent dangers of such action can be eliminated or at least minimized by the use of buoyed lines, booms indicating the outermost limits of the area.

Swimming and bathing areas in many rivers or streams are clearly defined by good-sized logs or booms chained or fastened together with heavy line; they provide adequate support or protection at any point in their length.

Line has also frequently been used to hold anchored resting buoys or floats in deep-water swimming areas. These small floats or watertight buoys are usually not large enough to climb up on, but merely provide a handhold for a tired swimmer. A life line looped around these buoys close to the surface will require less effort to grasp and hold onto until breath and strength are regained.

Because of water conditions at some surf beaches, the use of lines (three-quarter-inch), spiles (long poles) or buoys is an invaluable protective measure. The accompanying illustration shows a typical placement of such lines at a surf beach bathing area between two jetties.

Which of the following terms is familiar to you depends upon where you come from or where you are working as a lifeguard: land line, beach line, trail line or surf line. For our purpose here, all these terms mean the same thing—a one-quarter- or three-eighths-inch line varying in length from 200 to 600 feet or more depending on the water conditions and/or the bathing-area distance limits. To the outside end of the line, a sturdy galvanized or brass snap hook should be fastened by means of an eye splice. A thirty-inch shoulder halter or loop may also be spliced into this same end of the line. The line is used to haul the victim and lifeguard to safety after contact has been made. The balance of the line should be ready for quick, unhampered use. There are several ways that this can be done. The line

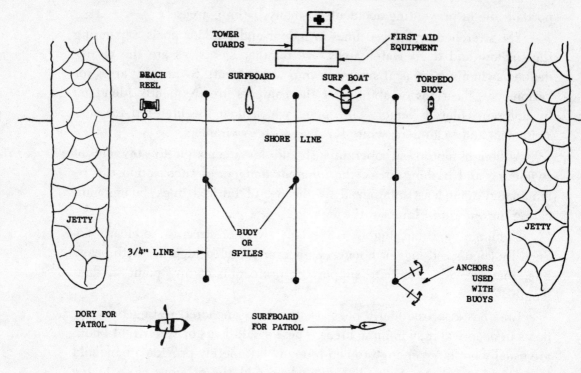

FIG. 19. TYPICAL PLACEMENT OF FIXED BEACH LINES

can be rolled on a reel. Here, too, experience and preferences have been deciding factors. There are types of reels which are fastened to lifeguard towers or stands; reels have been mounted on portable racks which can be carried closer to the rescue scene; reels have been fastened to sturdy posts placed in the sand at various positions along the beach; reels have been mounted on a sturdy piece of wood and with an attached wide leather or webbing provide a portable "chest" reel; on some of the larger beaches, reels have been mounted on jeeps, trucks and beach-buggies operated by members of the patrol.

Regardless of the preference, it is essential that the reel be free-running to avoid any undue drag on the lifeguard during his approach to the victim. Another possibility and source of chagrin is a backlash at the reel. This can occur when the line has not been wound rather snugly on the reel, leaving dangling loops at intervals along the line. These loops are easily rewound, backlashed or fouled on the reel if it is allowed to unwind faster than is necessary. It is important, therefore, that reels be attended by a second lifeguard.

Other effective methods in use today involve carefully coiled line in a small box, bushel basket or small butter tub. If coiled properly, the line will feed or pull out easily without snagging, snarling or fouling. A heavy canvas bag similar to those used by some coal-delivery men has also found preference with some beach patrols.

A good grade of one-quarter- or three-eighths-inch manila line should be used on reels or in the other devices. If heavy surf or strong currents are to be encountered, the three-eighths-inch line would be desired. The new synthetic fiber or plastic lines are excellent. They are lighter, stronger, will float, do not require drying after use, will not mildew or rot. Some of the synthetics and plastics are brightly colored, making the lines more visible.

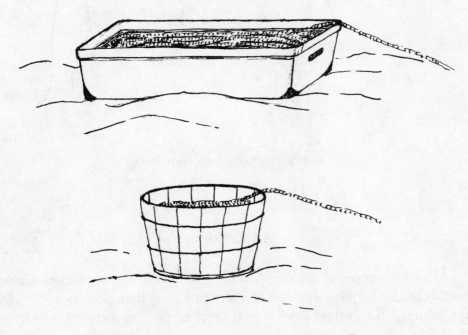

FIG. 20. BEACH LINE COILED IN BOX AND TUB

FIG. 21. BEACH LINE AND REEL

Aquascopes

The aquascope, water scope, water glass, look-box are common terms for this piece of equipment. It is of value in waters that are reasonably clear for scanning the bottom from a boat, float or dock to locate a submerged victim.

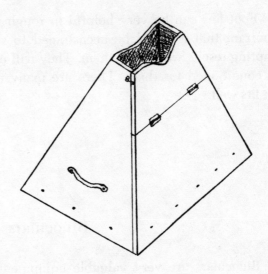

Fig. 22.   Aquascope

An aquascope and a powerful flashlight can be used effectively at night. The light should be held above the surface and directed downward alongside the 'scope.

Scanning the bottom over a large area with a water glass is a slow process. With the advent of swim fins, face masks and snorkels, the time required to do such a job was reduced considerably. This is highly important if the object of the search is a submerged victim.

Whistles

The police-type whistle is the badge of a lifeguard. If it is used properly, it is one of his most valuable pieces of equipment. It is used to warn people when they violate the safety rules or regulations, to warn them when they get near dangerous areas or currents and as a means of communication between guards. Use it meaningfully and sparingly.

Chrome-plated brass police-type whistles are generally used; however, some of the new plastic ones are good. They should be securely attached to a lanyard around the neck of the lifeguard. The lanyard should be short enough or adjustable so that the whistle cannot be easily lost.

Fins

Foot fins can be very helpful in rough water or strong currents. It is important that a guard be accustomed to swimming with fins before attempting rescue work with them. They will cause leg cramps if muscles are not conditioned for them. There are many types of fins. Choose the kind that fits well.

Binoculars

Binoculars are very valuable equipment for the lifeguard who must cover a large open body of water. They are particularly valuable when large crowds are in the water and on the beach. By using binoculars, the guard will be able to see clearly the actions and facial expressions of the people and be able to determine who is in trouble and what type of rescue or preventive action is indicated. Binoculars are also useful for checking on general surf and beach conditions. Rescues by other lifeguard stations can be watched to determine whether help is necessary.

Navy-type 7 x 50 binoculars are the most practical. Too high-powered binoculars or ones with a small field are very difficult to use.

Binoculars are precision optical instruments and must be treated with care. Any hard knock or fall can cause them to become unaligned or crack the lenses. They should not be left exposed to the sun or allowed to become wet or covered with sand. When not in use, they should be kept in their case.

6

RESCUES INVOLVING EQUIPMENT

Almost without exception, guards on surf beaches are required to use equipment when effecting a rescue. Flotation devices provide an opportunity to start artifical respiration in the water. They also provide a safe resting place for both the guard and victim. The uses of some of the more popular rescue devices are described in this chapter.

Rescue Buoy

The rescue buoy is a versatile piece of equipment. It can be used in many ways with a host of variations. The most efficient use of the buoy requires a crew of three lifeguards; however, it is still a very effective device for a single guard to use. A description of some of the techniques follows:

1. *One lifeguard with no land line (free buoy)*

   a) *Starting the rescue*

      (1) Keep your eye on the victim and keep calm.

      (2) Pick up the buoy, cast the loop of the towline over one shoulder and under the opposite arm, run to hard-packed sand and then to a point in front of the victim. On rip or run-out rescues, it is faster to hit the center of the current and swim with it. If there is a set or lateral current, the guard must enter the current above the victim so he will be carried to and not away from him.

      (3) When you enter the water, yell to other swimmers to get out of the water as you pass them. This will save you from rescuing additional swimmers and would-be lifeguards.

      (4) Best speed through the surf can be made by running until the water is about chest-deep, using the hands as paddles.

      (5) Dive under oncoming waves rather than swimming into them. If surf is large, cling to the bottom and pull yourself forward with your hands.

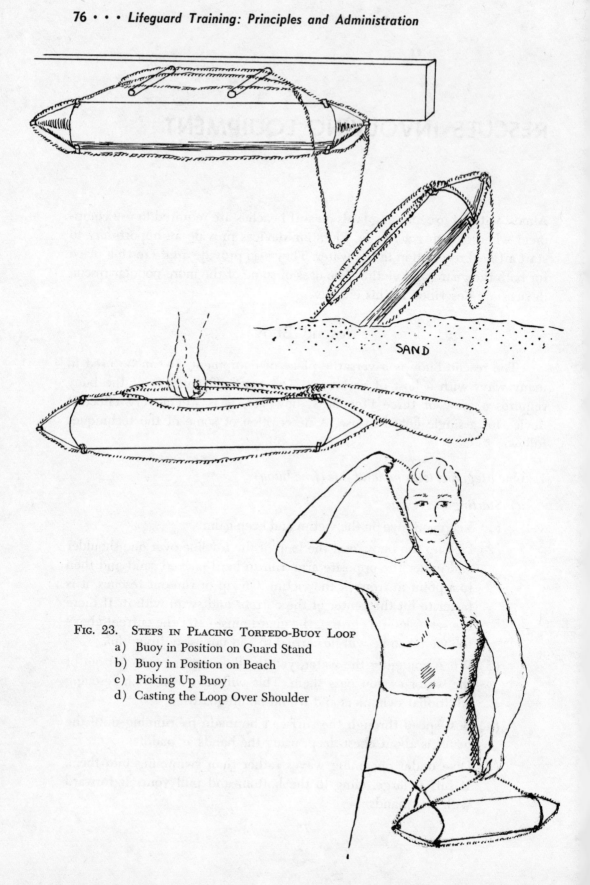

FIG. 23. STEPS IN PLACING TORPEDO-BUOY LOOP
  a) Buoy in Position on Guard Stand
  b) Buoy in Position on Beach
  c) Picking Up Buoy
  d) Casting the Loop Over Shoulder

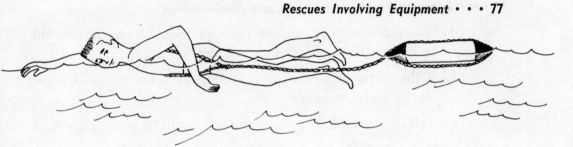

FIG. 24. TOWING TORPEDO BUOY TO VICTIM

b) *Approaching and reaching the victim*

(1) Make a mental note as to the location of the victim.

(2) Swim high so that you can see the victim; let him know that you are coming and tell him to hold on until you get there.

(3) On ordinary rescues stop short of the victim, avoid personal contact, push the buoy toward your victim from the side and allow him to seize the buoy and slide his head and chest up a little over the outer end, grasping the life lines at the sides of the buoy to maintain his position. After he has the buoy, assure him that everything is O.K. This gives him a chance to calm himself and gain a little rest and air. Now rest and plan your return to shore.

FIG. 25. EXTENDING BUOY TO VICTIM

(4) Watch the victim's eyes for panic or fright. Never let yourself be in a position in which he can grab you.

(5) If the victim is hysterical, it sometimes helps to use stronger, more forceful language.

(6) Tell the victim to hang onto the buoy until he reaches dry land.

(7) If the victim is unconscious or too exhausted to help himself in any way, a slightly different approach is necessary. In these cases, the rescuer should make a rear approach or front surface approach and follow with a cross-chest carry. By means of the towline, he can draw the buoy to him and, by putting his free arm over it, can rest and make slow headway toward shore, using his legs only. When rested, he can let the buoy go on its towline, ready to be used again should he tire.

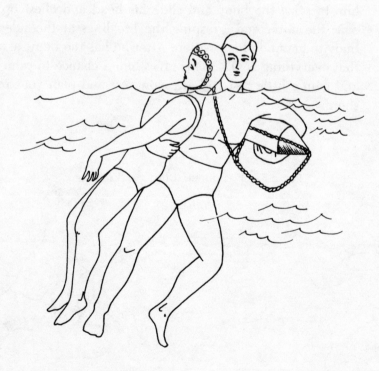

Fig. 26.   Resting With an Unconscious Victim

Fig. 27.   Towing a Conscious Victim

c) *Making a return to shore*

(1) After the victim is secure and the guard is rested, he can start swimming to shore, pulling the victim and buoy by the shoulder loop. The best stroke for this is a trudgen or breast stroke. You can also hold onto the can and swim a side stroke with a shallow arm pull.

Fig. 28.   Alternate Method of Towing Conscious Victim

(2) Keep looking over your shoulder to watch the waves and to make sure the victim is O.K. If the victim has a tendency to roll from side to side on the buoy, tell him to keep his legs spread apart and extended.

(3) Swim on about a forty-five degree angle when coming through strong runs or rips. Take advantage of the set or drift if there is any.

(4) Sometimes it is necessary or advisable to swim parallel to the beach. If you know a sand bar is near, head for it.

(5) In big surf, or when the victim is in bad shape, before each wave, hold the victim to the buoy and tell him to take a deep breath. When the wave hits, pinch his nose with your thumb and forefinger and keep your hand over his mouth to keep him from choking.

(6) If the victim is unconscious, use a cross-chest carry with your arm through the rope on the buoy.

2. *Two lifeguards with buoy and attached line*

   a) *Starting the rescue*

   (1) Follow all the steps in the preceding rescue.

   (2) The guard on shore will feed the line to the rescuer, holding it high to keep it out of the surf as much as possible.

FIG. 29. "FEEDING" THE BEACH LINE TO THE GUARD

FIG. 30.   EXTENDING BUOY TO VICTIM WITH BEACH LINE
ATTACHED

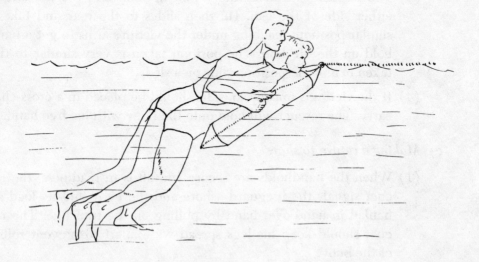

FIG. 31.   GUARD WITH CONSCIOUS VICTIM IN POSITION TO BE TOWED TOWARD
SHORE BY BEACH LINE

b) *Approaching the victim*

   (1) Approach is the same as in preceding rescues.

   (2) When making contact with the victim, be sure that he receives the opposite end from the one to which the land line is attached. If the victim takes the wrong end of the buoy, the land line will be to the rear. When the pull is taken, the buoy will be turned end-over-end. The victim's hold will be lost and there is a possibility of a head injury.

FIG. 32.   GUARD WITH UNCONSCIOUS VICTIM IN POSITION TO BE TOWED ASHORE BY BEACH LINE

   (3) The rescuer will direct the victim to hold onto the life line on either side of the can. He then slides to the rear and takes a similar position, reaching under the victim's arms to get a handhold on the life line. The position taken is very similar to that taken in a prone-position slide on a sled.

   (4) If the victim is unconscious, he should be placed in a cross-chest carry. The rescuer will hold onto the buoy with his free hand.

c) *Making a return to shore*

   (1) When the handholds are secure and all is in readiness, the rescuer signals the lifeguard ashore and the buoy and its load are hauled in hand-over-hand by pulling on the trail line. The rescuer should keep his legs spread wide apart to prevent rolling of the buoy.

   (2) The lineman plays a very important part in this type of rescue. He must play the line to take advantage of wave action, to hold

against adverse currents and to maintain those hanging onto the
buoy in reasonable comfort. He must handle the line himself
and direct such assistance as he may have. One of his major tasks
is to prevent onlookers laying hold of the line and running it up
the beach. In their eagerness to assist, these well-meaning persons can tear the buoy from the grasp of both the rescuer and
victim or pull them under the water.

(3) When shallow water is reached, the pull on the line must be
slackened so that the rescuing lifeguard can gain his footing and
assist the victim to shore. If the buoy and its load are pulled into
very shallow water, there is the danger of injury from heavy surf
action.

(4) After the rescue, the line should be rolled back on the reel or
coiled in its box.

3. *Combination rescue*

a) *One lifeguard and several victims*

(1) Tow the first victim to the second victim, then to shore; or

(2) Give first victim the buoy can, slip out of the loop, swim to the
second victim, tow him back to the can, then tow both victims
to shore; or

(3) Take two buoy cans when there are two or more victims in
trouble.

b) *Two or more guards with separate land lines (mass rescue)*

(1) Two guards swim with free buoys to the victims—another guard
swims out with or without another buoy.

(2) Upon reaching the victims and guards in the water, he helps
them fasten the buoys held by the victims to the land line.

(3) Guards then move behind victims and hold them securely on
the buoys.

(4) Upon a signal from the lifeguard who took out the land line, the
guard tending the line on shore will then pull the whole group
to safety.

4. *Rescues from breakwater and jetty*

a) Always walk, never run on rocks or rough ground to entrance point
near the victim.

b) This type of rescue presents an extreme hazard, both to the victim
and the lifeguard. It must be made with caution and good judgment.

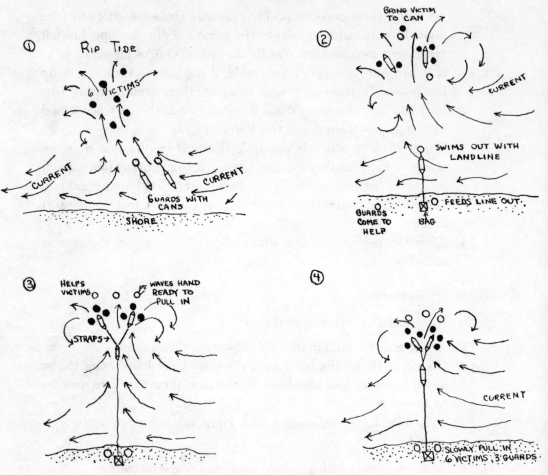

FIG. 33. METHODS OF GROUP RESCUE

(1) Always take a rescue buoy.

(2) Never dive from any height.

(3) Always pick deepest water to make entrance.

(4) Pick as clear an area as possible (no submerged rocks or pilings).

c) *Entrance to small surf*

(1) Enter immediately after a wave has broken.

(2) Enter water and walk until about waist-deep, then belly-flop with the buoy thrown to one side.

(3) Swim clear of the hazardous area, taking advantage of the back flow of water.

d) *Entrance to large surf*
    (1) Be careful of being washed off the rocks, watch for unusually large sets of waves.
    (2) Be especially careful. Enter at the deepest spot, use a belly-flop and take advantage of the backwash of the waves.
    (3) If washed onto the rocks, relax your body as much as possible. Use the buoy as a fender between you and the rocks.

e) After making contact with the victim, tow him out from the rocks in any direction that you can by taking advantage of whatever currents are present.

f) If washed onto the rocks with a victim, use him as a fender between you and the rocks. A dead or injured lifeguard is of no value to the victim.

5. *Rescue from piers or docks in the surf*
    a) Rescue time can sometimes be reduced by using a pier to effect deep-water rescues.
    b) Run on pier to vicinity of victim.
    c) Throw the rescue buoy near the victim.
    d) Make sure water is deep enough and that there are no submerged pilings.
    e) Jump feet first, keep legs crossed *(never dive)*.
    f) Make contact with victim and tow him to safety.

FIG. 34.   APPROACH TO VICTIM FROM PIER

6. *Piling rescues under pier*

   a) Enter the water to take advantage of the outgoing currents, which are generally present alongside or underneath the pier.

   b) Personal safety requires the approaching guard to keep alert and clear of pilings. When under the pier, swim in the center between the pilings.

   c) Swim into the piling area during intervals between the waves.

   d) When approaching the victim, watch for incoming surf; keep away from the area directly in front of pilings when moving in to the victim.

   e) Upon reaching the victim, tell him to let go of the piling and grab the can.

   f) If he refuses:

      (1) Cover the victim's mouth and nose with one hand.

      (2) Grab the victim's hair with the other hand, lean back and pull hard.

      (3) Place the buoy under the victim's arms and chest as soon as you have him free of the piling.

   g) Tow the victim clear of the pilings in whatever direction the currents will make easiest, then head for shore.

FIG. 35.   FREEING VICTIM FROM PIER

h) Use the buoy as a fender to protect the victim from the pilings, should breaking surf be encountered.

i) When necessary, use the buoy and the victim as fenders to protect yourself from the pilings. The victim may drown if the guard is injured.

Boat Rescue

The placement and preparation of a rowboat for rescue work will vary in different parts of the country, depending upon whether the lifeguard is on duty at a calm lake or river beach or at a surf beach. Regardless, speed in launching and getting under way is essential.

The oars in a "rescue" boat should be left in the rowlocks, blades outboard, looms inboard with the grips resting on the bottom of the boat behind the rowing seat, and the throat of the oar in the rowlock. Some guards prefer to place the oars on the thwarts with the blades extending toward the stern, ready to place into the rowlocks as soon as they are launched and seated.

For quick launching, the boat should be moored (to a dock) or beached with the bow pointing "seaward." If water conditions will permit, the boat should be completely afloat or as nearly so as is practical. Obviously, at most ocean beaches this is not possible. At these locations, the boats may be seen resting on top of one or more rollers as close to the water as conditions will permit. Here again, preferences and experience have been deciding factors concerning the length, size and construction of the rollers. Some prefer solid wooden rollers, others prefer elongated, inflatable tubes. Still others prefer to have their boats resting on two-wheeled trailers. The size and type of boat and the beach itself, hard or soft sand, are also factors in deciding what device shall be used for launching.

At lake and other calm-water beaches, it is not an uncommon practice for one lifeguard to launch and effectively handle the boat. At surf beaches with vastly different water conditions, plus the larger and heavier boats, at least two or more guards are required for good launchings. Here is where good instruction, much practice and teamwork pay off.

When a beached boat is needed to assist a swimmer in flat water, the lifeguard should run to the boat, push out on the stern or transom until the boat is completely afloat, jump in over the stern and take his rowing position quickly before way is lost. While rowing, look over a shoulder, keep eyes on victim. Unless the water is very calm and there's no wind or cur-

Fig. 36. If Contact Is Made at Side of the Boat, Victim Should Be Restrained From Boarding and Be Led to the Stern for Proper Boarding

rent to contend with, approach the victim on the leeward side to avoid drifting down over him. When the rescuer is still some distance away, a ring buoy can be tossed to the victim for support. If a line is attached to the buoy, the victim can be pulled in to the stern of the boat. If there is another victim farther out, the ring buoy will provide support for the first victim while the boat proceeds out for a pickup of the other victim, and then returns for the victim closest to shore. This technique has been used many times by the Atlantic City Beach Patrol, when there have been multiple swimmers in difficulty. The accuracy of side-arm and over-the-shoulder throws of ring buoys by the guards appears uncanny.

Another successful procedure has been to wait until the victim is about ten feet away, then to extend the rescue pole. If the distance is shorter than this, an oar can be extended. The victim is then pulled around to the stern of the boat. It is usually advisable to use extensions in one of these ways instead of reaching for the victim with your hands. Some beach patrols using the double-ender surfboat with a crew of three or four for launchings and rowing prefer to make a quick pickup of a victim from and over the side of the boat. Again, practice and teamwork are essential.

If a victim is unable to grasp an extended pole or an oar, the rescuer may approach him stern first and then grasp his hands. He can be held to the stern by crossing his arms over the transom and holding his wrists down. If the victim cannot be assisted or lifted into the boat over the stern or the guard cannot hold the victim to the stern and row at the same time, he can then tie the victim to the stern by passing a line around his chest, under both arms and secure the line to a thwart, completing the rescue by rowing and towing the victim to shore.

All this should indicate why at least two guards are necessary to man a boat for patrol and rescue work. While one rows, the other may sit or stand in the stern, facing the swimmers during patrol. Both guards should keep their eyes constantly on the swimmers; see everything that happens; be alert to possible signals from other guards on the tower or stand and be ready to give calm, deliberate, intelligent assistance when and where it is needed.

Following a boat rescue in flat waters, the return to the dock or beach usually requires nothing more than straight-away rowing. In surf waters, however, the safest method of coming ashore is to back in with the bow of the boat headed into the waves, thus permitting much better control. A bow-first return with the boat riding the forward slope of a breaking wave jeopardizes good control and the safety of the crew and rescued victim. Therefore no attempt should be made to ride a wave to shore when the boat is in use for patrol or rescue work. An improperly handled boat can also be a menace to nearby bathers and is a poor example of a corps' or patrol's efficiency. Contrarywise, good boat-handling and seamanship are spectacular, attracting public attention. This is to be desired and can be achieved only by much pre-season and in-service work. The need for this becomes more of a necessity if the particular-type boat in use by a corps is one requiring a crew of four men for rowing and a fifth man in the stern as coxswain. The coxswain should be in complete command of the boat. He will steer, call all boat commands and otherwise assume responsibility for the safety of the boat, crew and nearby bathers. During patrol, he will keep the boat moving on a course as close to the outer line of bathers as safe handling will permit. For appearance's sake and because it may be necessary to go overboard quickly, it is recommended that the crew not wear sweat shirts, jackets or any other outer clothing. At all times, the crew's conduct should be beyond reproach.

Launching and boarding boats involving a crew and coxswain require a procedure other than that described earlier for a single lifeguard in a flat-water rescue.

The following procedure is recommended: prior to the launching, each man should take his place along the side of the boat, opposite the position he will take as oarsman. If the boat is ready for launching, the oars, with blades toward the bow, are lying in the boat against the sides and the rowlocks are ready for quick placement in their sockets (thole pins may already be in place). Some patrols prefer to leave their oars along the sides of the boat; others place the oars along the center line. The trim of the boat should also be considered before launching. In surf work, the distribution of the

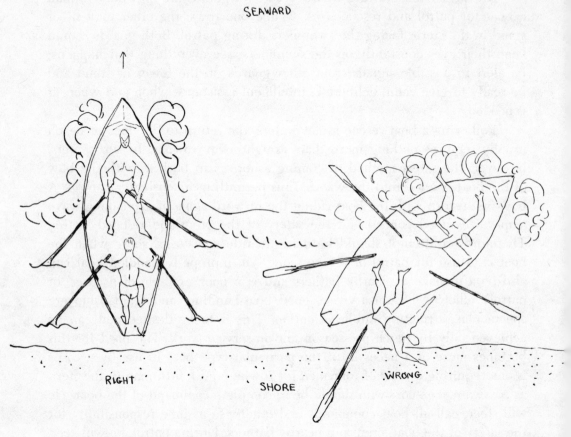

FIG. 37. KEEP SURFBOAT AT RIGHT ANGLE TO WAVES AT ALL TIMES

crew's weight should permit a light bow, better enabling the boat to rise through incoming waves. When the boat has been launched, the oarsmen should vault over the sides and take their positions. In the meantime, the coxswain has remained out of the boat, at the stern, holding it in position. At his command, "Stand by," the oarsmen position their rowlocks and oars, and are ready for the next command. Once aboard, the coxswain should quickly put his oar in the water for steering or a necessary fend-off. With the command "Together give way," the crew will row ahead in unison with the stroke oarsman. The first few, perhaps three, strokes should be short and fast in order to give the boat some momentum, then lengthened to a longer, full stroke. No further information concerning the various commands and maneuvers will be included in this chapter, for we believe these will be acquired during the lifeguards' pre-season training. It is also during this period that frequent rough surf conditions can provide the opportunity to develop procedures to cope with swampings and upsets. Many upsets have been prevented by each member of the crew sliding over the high side of the boat—the side that is being pushed high by a breaking wave. In addition to forcing the boat back to an even keel and averting a capsize, this also places the crew in the best position to clear the boat if it does capsize.

If the coxswain should give the command "All out," the crew should jump or dive clear of the boat immediately after they have placed the rowlocks inboard and tossed the oars from the boat as far as possible. These are important steps to be taken to prevent possible serious injury. Many other aspects of good seamanship become familiar to the new lifeguard as he progresses through the pre-season training with the more experienced members of his beach patrol.

Surfboard and Paddleboard Rescues

The surfboard or paddleboard is a very fine piece of rescue equipment when used by a trained person. It is one of the fastest, most stable and easily maneuverable pieces of equipment created by man. It can be used for patroling around a swimming area or in among swimmers. It cannot be swamped and the new solid foam and fiber glass boards cannot leak and need almost no maintenance. There are no oars to be lost or broken, and positive flotation for rescuer and victims is always assured. However, it does take some training and experience to safely and effectively use a surf or paddle board for rescue work.

The surfboard, when introduced to the mainland of the United States by George Freeth in 1907, was chiefly a wave-riding device. The board was solid, approximately nine feet long, twenty-two inches wide and quite heavy. It also had a square tail. In 1928, Thomas Blake introduced the hollow stream-lined pointed-tail surfboard, which he used in winning a paddling championship race in Hawaii.

The revolution in plastic has now produced surfboards with many highly scientific forms and shapes for all types of wave and wake riding and rescue work. Boards which are extremely light in weight, rugged in construction, beautiful to look at and reasonable in cost are now appearing by the hundreds on all our surf beaches and are beginning to be seen on inland beaches as well.

An experienced surf or paddle board user can effect a rescue in any type of water and under any condition which would thwart the average lifeguard. The lengths of boards vary from eight to fourteen feet with thicknesses up to five inches, and can be effectively used for lifesaving and rescue purposes. The experienced user could save one or twenty victims with ease, if he were confronted with tired and willing victims. In the case of the unconscious or submerged victim, the situation presents a condition which requires careful planning and operation.

To rescue a submerged victim, the rescuer must leave the board to recover the victim. In quiet waters he can leave the board and perform his surface dive without fear of having the board moved out of his immediate reach. In rough or ocean water, leaving the board under such conditions would be foolhardy. To keep the board within reach, rescuers attach a light line to the board's tail and then loop the free end over their shoulders in a halter fashion. Of course, they allow about twenty feet of line for freedom of movement and for deep diving to reach the victim if need be. Once they come to the surface, the experienced board man will pull the board to him, then mount it while holding onto the victim and then place the victim on the board.

In rescuing the tired swimmer, the approach can be made from either side depending on the way the paddler would like to effect the rescue.

Lying in a prone position and paddling as quickly as possible with your head up in order to obtain a clear view of the subject on approach, grasp the nearest hand or wrist. As soon as you make contact, sit upright on the board. This will stop your forward progress. The next step is to place the victim's arms on the board, holding the wrists in front of you. Tell the victim to relax and rest, and speak words of encouragement to him. This next step depends upon the condition of the victim. If he is able, he may climb on the board himself; if not, you will probably have to assist him.

It is important that the board be turned around and headed towards shore before the victim is placed on it.

In paddling towards shore, the rescuer should assume a position as far back as possible in order to keep the nose of the board up; he should also drag his feet to stabilize the board. Don't be in too much of a hurry to come ashore.

In the ocean, pick your spot when the waves are at a lull. If a wave is going to break on you and the victim, sit upright on the board at its approach. Hold onto the sides of the board with your hands and legs, and when the wave breaks, you will receive a slow and slight forward push. However, if the board is allowed to get broadside to the wave, either coming in or going out, disaster will occur.

In rescuing a helpless victim, approach him from either side. Grasp his nearest hand or wrist and sit upright on the board. To place the victim on the board, bring his body level with the board by placing your right or left leg, depending on the side he is on, in the stomach area and raise his body up slowly until it is level with the board.

Once the victim is across the board, reach across and grasp his outside arm and place it on the board. Be gentle and careful, and slide the victim forward until his body is lengthwise on the board with his legs resting across your thighs. Once you obtain this position, grasp the leg that is nearest you and bend back and assume a tandem prone position. Place the victim's hands under his head. Prone pressure method of artificial respiration can be performed in this position. Mouth-to-mouth artificial respiration can also be performed on a surf or paddle board as described in Chapter 8. Keep your feet in the water for stablization and paddle to shore, being careful at all times to maneuver the board at right angles to the oncoming and breaking waves.

Ocean or surf work presents a whole new challenge which calls for a thorough knowledge of the sea, wave action, currents and turbulent water. This phase calls for split-second timing, sound judgment and excellent physical condition. Much experience is necessary to cope with the problems the surf presents. The two most important things to remember in using a board in the surf is to keep the board at right angles to the waves at all times and to keep the bow up.

To summarize, to make rescues with a surf or paddle board one must be a good swimmer, have knowledge of all forms of water rescue and water conditions, have a good sense of balance and have experience in using a surf or paddle board.

Fig. 38.   Surfboard

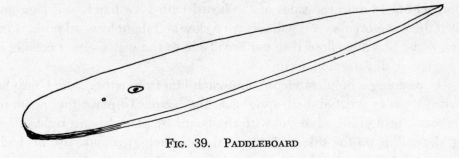

Fig. 39. Paddleboard

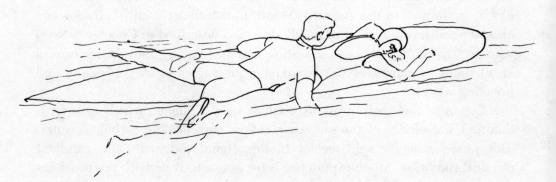

Fig. 40. Position for Rescue

Fig. 41. Group Support

7

SWIMMING RESCUES AND ASSISTS WITHOUT EQUIPMENT

Although it is generally agreed by lifesaving experts that the simplest way to effect a rescue is to "extend your reach," there may be times when it is more practical to make a swimming rescue. It is at such times that *judgment* is the key which determines exactly what the lifeguard does. A common example of this involves a guard at a large outdoor, heavily populated pool. The guard is at his post on a permanent stand with a large canvas-covered cork ring buoy hanging alongside. The need for a rescue or an assist arises. The potential victim is not so far away that the buoy couldn't easily be tossed to him as a free-floating support. Because there are several other swimmers very close to the victim, there is a possibility that the buoy might hit and injure someone. The ring buoy is not tossed. Instead, the guard resorts to a swimming rescue without equipment, immediately following his whistle signal to alert the other guards.

Whether or not a regular approach and carry such as the guard learned in his lifesaving course would be used, is a question. Because the distance from the trouble spot to safety in a swimming pool is usually short, the following methods of assist or rescue have proven to be highly effective:

1. *Reaching assist:* those methods taught in the regular lifesaving courses can be used more frequently than other methods of assist. A common variation of the basic hand extension, from the deck, has the guard jumping into the water, holding onto the side of the pool or the overflow trough with one hand and extending the other hand or "outside" leg to the victim, and then pulling him to the side of the pool.

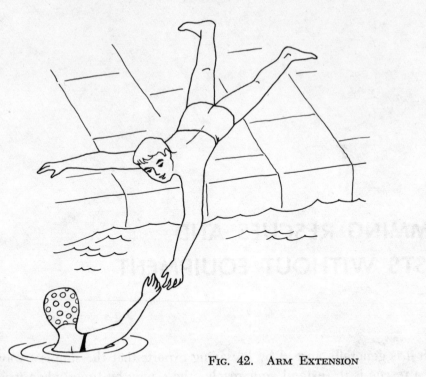

FIG. 42.   ARM EXTENSION

FIG. 43.   LEG EXTENSION

FIG. 44.   POLE EXTENSION

2. *Bottom push:* the guard merely goes below the victim and pushes him to safety while standing on the bottom. This is usually done when the victim is not close enough to the pool's side for a reaching rescue or the guard has had to dive in and swim a short distance to the victim. Since the victim is usually close to shallow water or to the side of the pool, the rescuer can easily stand on the bottom, grasp the victim by the feet or legs and shove him to shallow water or up into contact with the side of the pool. The guard immediately surfaces and completes the rescue by making certain the victim is back in shallow water or holding to the side. Other swimmers will probably assist in this rescue.

FIG. 45. BOTTOM PUSH

FIG. 46.   UNDERARM ASSIST

3.   *Underarm assist:* employed many times for a small child or a swimmer in difficulty but not panicky. The guard merely swims up to the victim and grasps him under one arm, close to the armpit, and swims side stroke while supporting the victim a short distance to safety.

4.   *Chin tow:* sometimes used when the person in trouble is facing away from safety. The guard merely executes a rear approach, grasps the chin and tows the victim the short distance necessary. This is an elementary rescue which is quite simply performed by an experienced guard.

FIG. 47.   CHIN TOW

5. *Hair or chin tow:* used when bringing someone from the bottom to the surface of the water. The guard may use both hands on the chin of the person or grab the hair and push from the bottom toward the side of the pool. If the distance is such that some swimming is necessary, the lifeguard may elect to use the cross-chest carry right from the bottom and all the way to the nearest egress from the pool.

Fig. 48. Cross-Chest Carry With Wrist Lock for Struggling Victim

6. *Standard approaches and carries:* should be employed in some of the extremely large outdoor pools when a swimmer gets in trouble too far away for the usual methods of assist to be satisfactory or when the victim is panicky or large. The lifeguard should take no chances, but should employ a standard method of approach and carry according to the situation, especially with adult-size victims.

In a good lifeguard organization, these methods will all be practiced, and problems involving their use will be part of a training program. Rescues that are actually made should be written up with part of the report explaining the "technique" that was used. This, then, can be used for future training and discussion on rescues and will be of especial importance in training new lifeguards.

FIG. 49. WRIST TOW

One-Man Rescues Under Flat-Water Conditions

There is no doubt that the long-established methods of approaching, making contact, leveling off and carrying a victim have saved lives. In all instances involving a single victim and single potential rescuer, the time spent in mastering those skills during a formal lifesaving course has paid big dividends. Because all situations requiring lifeguard action are not exactly the same, these factors should be considered when making the rescue:

1. Condition of victim (panicky, exhausted, unconscious, etc.)
2. Nearest shallow-water area
3. Size of victim
4. Distance to shore
5. Boat or other rescue devices on the way

In considering these factors, let us examine each, individually. *The condition of the victim* when the guard makes his approach will have a big bearing upon what the guard elects to do. If the victim is struggling but is still able to keep his head above water and get his breath, it may be only necessary for the guard to approach to the point of being "just out of reach" and then, by talking to the victim, give him instructions and encouragement to swim his way in to safety. Many times, a swimmer in trouble can be "talked in" by a guard who uses a little psychology. This type of rescue keeps the guard from making personal contact and provides a "moral victory" in that the victim overcomes his difficulties with a little encouragement and makes his own way to safety. This will give the victim a sense of accomplishment as well as a good object lesson in getting out of trouble. Many weak swimmers get into trouble by letting their feet down to touch bottom and, finding no bottom there, immediately start struggling in a vertical position. The guard then talks them into getting their feet up and swimming on in to shore. Should the victim be in a state of panic, and therefore unable to listen to reason, the guard will then have to use the normal approach technique for the situation as it confronts him and a cross-chest carry for control. In some cases where the person is on the very edge of shallow water but unable to reach it, the guard may only have to go to the bottom and give a boost toward shallow water. This type of assist with a panicky victim is often employed where the victim finds himself "just out of reach" of the shallow area. The guard may employ a surface dive to get away from the reach of the victim, plant his feet firmly on the bottom, grasp the victim around the legs and give him a good thrust forward to the shallow area. The victim will probably swim a few feet farther to safety because of the impetus of the push and the fact that his feet will have been pushed up to a swimming position. The guard will then merely follow through to assist the victim from the water onto land, where he may have to be treated for shock and exhaustion as a result of his struggling efforts.

The nearest shallow-water area sometimes will have an effect on where the guard will take the victim. In some instances, an offshore sand bar will create water of standing depth to which the victim could be taken. Sometimes a number of shallow-water areas are formed in the same manner a considerable distance from shore. In any event, the victim is usually taken to the nearest shallow-water area to wait for boat transference back to the beach. If the victim is in a semi-conscious state, then the rescuer has no alternative but to get the victim to shore as quickly as possible, using the fastest-type carry he can employ. The distance to nearest shallow water may be only a few feet whereas the distance back to shore may be fifty to a hundred feet or more. The option of whether to go to shallow water or back to shore will depend entirely on the condition of the victim and whether or not the guard has a boat, surfboard or other rescue devices on the way to assist in removal.

The size of the victim as well as the degree of panic will have a great deal of bearing on the type of approach and carry or assist that the guard will employ. A child many times can readily be assisted by the guard swimming alongside and holding him under one arm while he swims side stroke to support the child. The child will, through the assist, be able to employ some swimming efforts of his own to return to safety. In such a case, the guard merely swims to the side of the child and grasps him under the arm at the armpit, allowing the child to swim on his stomach or back while the guard swims alongside, giving support and encouragement. There are cases where adults will respond readily to this technique of a tired-swimmer assist. If the person is merely tired and needs support for a short distance, this method is much easier to employ than the regular tired-swimmer carry, which is sometimes tried by inexperienced guards only to have it fail because the victim does not know how to follow directions or cannot understand them. In the "underarm assist," it is important that the guard observe the person carefully to watch for signs of panic, which might cause the victim to grasp the guard in a hold. In some cases of small children becoming panicky, the guard may elect to let the child grasp him and hang on while the guard merely swims either on his back or stomach and gives the child a "piggyback" type of ride to safety. Naturally, this is not recommended for larger persons. If the victim is a large youngster or adult, then the best rescue will be one of the effective control carries as a matter of self-protection against possible panic. The matter of transference from an underarm assist to a control carry is not difficult but should be practiced during workout sessions.

The distance to shore will have an effect on the type of rescue employed by the guard. At most well-organized beaches, there will be a boat in the vicinity that is used for patrolling and rescue. However, when the boat is not close to the area of trouble, the guard will have to perform a swimming rescue. If the proper alert signal has been given, the boat can be directed toward the trouble to prevent the guard from having to employ a long-distance rescue of perhaps fifty to a hundred feet or more. If the distance to shore is greater than the distance to another shallow-water area, it may be wiser to elect to go to the nearest shallow water. If there is no shallow water, then the guard must be prepared to return to shore. He will find that it will be most helpful to be able to switch sides in a distance carry to obtain relief and maintain the best control over the victim. In practice, it is important to learn to carry on the left side as well as the right side and to perform the switch-over with the greatest amount of control possible. The guard should also remember that, if he is to be called on to perform a long-distance carry, he must use an approach stroke that will not tire him out, yet get him to the victim as quickly as possible. This approach stroke will vary with each guard's ability. One guard may use a high head crawl or trudgen crawl while another will find his best approach, in order to have good reserve, will be a breast stroke or trudgen.

Boat or other rescue apparatus on the way will be a factor determining whether or not the guard will attempt to perform a swimming rescue. In most cases, the guard will put the person in a carry or support and wait for the boat. If the person in trouble needs control, then a cross-chest carry must be employed with the guard only swimming in place to support the victim until the boat arrives. If the victim is only tired, then the guard may elect to place him on his back and then, by treading water alongside the victim, support him with one or both hands. The guard may also employ the underarm support while swimming alongside the victim and work toward the boat or other rescue device on the way. In many cases, the guard will not have to make personal contact with the victim if the victim is only tired. His presence will offer psychological support and he will be able to talk to the victim and get him to assist himself until the rescue apparatus arrives.

One-Man Rescues Under Rough-Water Conditions

In rough-water conditions, most rescues can be avoided by proper supervision of the swimming area and by keeping swimmers in shallower water. In effect, this is part of preventive lifeguarding. If rescues are then needed, as in the case of a person being unable to regain footing, even in water of normal standing depth, the guard will not have difficulty in rendering assistance. In a rough-water rescue, the guard will have to employ the proper approach and carry for the condition of the victim. In most cases, this will be either a front surface approach or a rear approach followed by a cross-chest carry. Underwater approaches are difficult because of possible shallow water depth at low wave level (in the trough) and poor visibility under water. It is essential that practice rescues be made in rough-water conditions so that the guard will know what he can expect. Physical fitness is most important in rough water, as all of the guard's strength and ability will be needed even in a short rescue. Wave conditions will generally be found only in the larger lakes, although some inland lakes will develop a fair amount of wave or high chop under certain conditions. It will also be important to the guard to know, for each day, the direction of flow and amount of current being generated, as it may have a definite effect on direction of rescue. This can only be determined by the guard entering the water and checking conditions for himself.

Two-Man Rescues

There may be conditions where two guards can perform a rescue more easily and with a higher degree of safety. If the victim appears to be a large person or is in a state of panic that will make handling almost impossible, it will be better if two men perform the rescue. This type of rescue can also be used in rough water if two guards are available.

The technique of approach to the victim is the same as any technique with both guards stopping, as usual, prior to contacting the victim. The two guards then approach from opposite sides of the victim and grasp him under the armpits while employing a side stroke, facing him. This supports the victim between two rescuers and gives more-effective control. The victim may be placed either on his back or stomach as the situation dictates. In rough water, it will be better to have the victim on his back to prevent his face being submerged during the rescue.

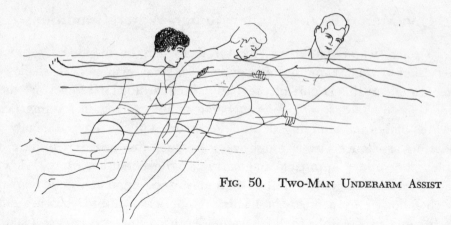

FIG. 50.   TWO-MAN UNDERARM ASSIST

Human-Chain Rescues

In cases of rough water, a regular human-chain rescue may be employed as practiced in the basic training for lifeguard candidates. This requires the ability of the guard to organize persons who are on the beach and direct the procedure with the greatest amount of proficiency. The success of the human-chain rescue will be determined by the organizational ability of the lifeguard and the availability of people who can swim well enough to participate. Consider the implications if many more children and adults who frequent the large bathing areas at inland lakes and beaches could be taught to swim better, rather than just dunk and wade, and also have some prior knowledge of the procedure for effecting a human-chain rescue.

FIG. 51.   HUMAN CHAIN

8

ARTIFICIAL RESPIRATION
AND OTHER FIRST-AID MEASURES

Drownings may be either active or passive. The person seized with a heart attack or other medical problems, rendered unconscious by fainting or by a blow, seized by a violent cramp or paralyzed by fear may simply slip beneath the surface without warning, in direct contrast to the easily recognized signs of distress. Increasing evidence that passive drownings exceed those of the active type means that a much keener, more alert vigilance by lifeguards is essential—"keep counting heads."

The exhausted or panicky bather will usually continue to stay on the surface for a few moments and by his convulsive agitation, advertise the fact that he is drowning. His movements will be either violently or feebly unrelated to each other, depending on the amount of energy he possesses, causing him to bob up and down until finally, with tidal air depleted, he settles beneath the surface and starts downward.

If the tidal air is lost on the first downward trip and he can make no move to rise again, he will not of his own volition reappear at the surface. On the other hand, if he manages to hold some tidal air on each downward trip and can still make frantic clawing efforts to return to the surface, the chances are he will reappear one or more times.

Whatever the case, when enough tidal air escapes from the lungs to cause the specific gravity of the body to be greater than that of the water it displaces, the person starts downward. The rate at which the body descends is in exact proportion to its specific gravity but may be affected and deviated from the perpendicular by currents. As the body descends, the increasing pressure of the water on the chest walls forces out the remainder of the tidal air in a thin stream of bubbles. On occasion, the glottis may be in spasm, and when it is finally released, the remaining air may be lost in one great bubbling exhalation.

107

Artificial Respiration

Because "time" is such a vital factor in all cases of asphyxia, it is essential that an apparently drowned victim be given artificial respiration promptly. At most indoor and outdoor swimming pools this should not be a problem. At outdoor areas (lakes, rivers, bays, ocean) where rescues may involve greater distances from shore and possibly an underwater recovery of the victim, artificial respiration should be started as soon as the victim is brought to the surface, before and/or during the return to shore.

The use of flotation devices as rescue equipment and minor adaptations of the mouth-to-mouth method of artificial respiration provide a practical, effective solution to this problem (see Figs. 53–55, pp. 110–11).

Of the several known methods of artificial respiration, the three that are most often used include the mouth-to-mouth or mouth-to-nose method; the chest-pressure–arm-lift (Silvester) method; and the back-pressure–arm-lift (Holger-Nielsen) method.

MOUTH-TO-MOUTH (MOUTH-TO-NOSE) METHOD

If there is foreign matter visible in the mouth, wipe it out quickly with your fingers or a cloth wrapped around your fingers.

1. Tilt the head back so the chin is pointing upward. Pull or push the jaw into a jutting-out position.

   These maneuvers should relieve obstruction of the airway by moving the base of the tongue away from the back of the throat.

2. Open your mouth wide and place it tightly over the victim's mouth. At the same time pinch the victim's nostrils shut or close the nostrils with your cheek. Or close the victim's mouth and place your mouth over the nose. Blow into the victim's mouth or nose. (Air may be blown through the victim's teeth, even though they may be clenched.)

   The first blowing efforts should determine whether or not obstruction exists.

3. Remove your mouth, turn your head to the side and listen for the return rush of air that indicates air exchange. Repeat the blowing effort.

   For an adult, blow vigorously at the rate of about twelve breaths per minute. For a child, take relatively shallow breaths appropriate for the child's size, at the rate of about twenty per minute.

4. If you are not getting air exchange, recheck the head and jaw position. If you still do not get air exchange, quickly turn victim

Fig. 52. Mouth-to-Mouth (Mouth-to-Nose) Resuscitation

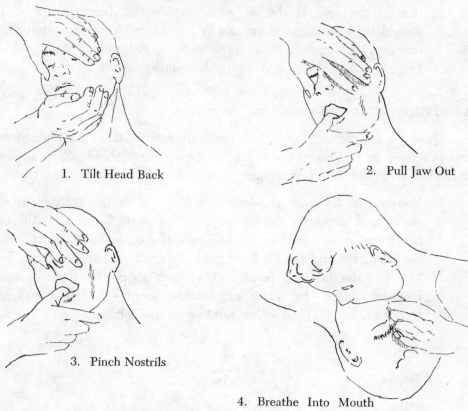

1. Tilt Head Back

2. Pull Jaw Out

3. Pinch Nostrils

4. Breathe Into Mouth

on his side and administer several sharp blows between the shoulder blades in the hope of dislodging foreign matter.

Again sweep your fingers through the victim's mouth to remove foreign matter.

Those who do not wish to come in contact with the person may hold a cloth over the victim's mouth or nose and breathe through it. The cloth does not greatly affect the exchange of air.

MOUTH-TO-MOUTH TECHNIQUE FOR INFANTS AND SMALL CHILDREN

If foreign matter is visible in the mouth, clean it out quickly as described previously.

1. Place the child on his back and use the fingers of both hands to lift the lower jaw from beneath and behind, so that it juts out.
2. Place your mouth over the child's mouth *and* nose, making a relatively leakproof seal, and breathe into the child, using shallow puffs of air. The breathing rate should be about twenty breaths per minute.

If you meet resistance in your blowing efforts, recheck the position of the jaw. If the air passages are still blocked, the child should be suspended momentarily by the ankles or inverted over one arm and given two or three sharp pats between the shoulder blades, in the hope of dislodging obstructing matter.

ADAPTATION OF MOUTH-TO-MOUTH TECHNIQUE

Once the simple steps of mouth-to-mouth resuscitation are understood and practiced in the classroom or on the beach, they should be practiced in the following simulated situations:

1. *Victim and Rescuer in Water.* In deep water the rescuer treads water and supports the face-up, unconscious "victim" with one hand under the shoulder blades; with the other hand, pinch "victims" nostrils and tilt his head back. Rescuer executes a strong leg kick to raise his own head high enough to permit the rhythmic blowing action. In water of shoulder depth or less the same technique can be used while standing on the bottom.

FIG. 53. MOUTH-TO-MOUTH RESUSCITATION IN THE WATER

2. *Boat and Single Rescuer.* The rescuer brings the "victim" to the side or stern of boat in a regular lifesaving carry; grasps the boat with one hand and supports "victim's" body in a face-up position on his thigh and knee. The free hand is used to pinch the "victim's" nostrils and tilt his head back.

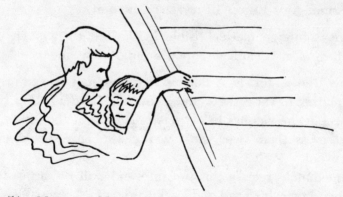

FIG. 54.   MOUTH-TO-MOUTH RESUSCITATION ALONGSIDE BOAT, DOCK
OR AT POOLSIDE

3. *Boat, Surfboard or Canoe.* A single rescuer can quickly take a prone
position across the boat, surfboard or canoe. With his head and
arms over the side, the rescuer supports the "victim" behind the
neck with one hand and pinches the nostrils and tilts the head
back with the other hand.

FIG. 55.   MOUTH-TO-MOUTH RESUSCITATION WITH VICTIM SUPPORTED BY
TORPEDO BUOY

4. *Single Rescuer With Torpedo Buoy.* In this simulated situation, the
rescuer makes personal contact with the "victim" and places him in
the face-up position. The torpedo (or diamond) buoy is then brought
into position *across* the "victim's" chest and his arm placed over
the buoy. With the buoy now providing full support of the "victim,"
the rescuer can now perform mouth-to-mouth resuscitation as in
Figure 55. *Note:* If a rescue tube is used, the rescuer can begin
resuscitation as soon as the "victim" has been contacted and the
tube is in position around the "victim's" body.

CHEST-PRESSURE–ARM-LIFT (SILVESTER) METHOD

If there is foreign matter visible in the mouth, wipe it out quickly with your fingers or a cloth wrapped around your fingers.

1. Place the victim in a face-up position; put something under his shoulders to raise them and allow the head to drop backward.
2. Kneel at the victim's head, grasp his arms at the wrists, cross them and press them over the lower chest. This should cause air to flow out.
3. Immediately release this pressure and pull the arms outward and upward over his head and backward as far as possible. This should cause air to rush in.
4. Repeat this cycle about twelve times per minute, checking the mouth frequently for obstructions.

FIG. 56. CHEST-PRESSURE–ARM-LIFT METHOD OF RESUSCITATION

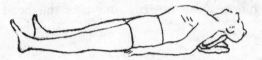

1. Position of Victim

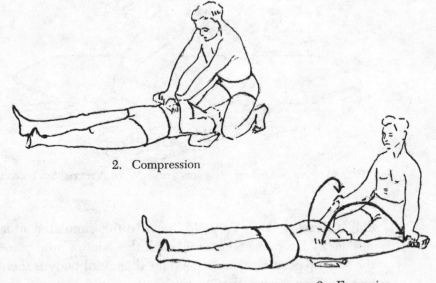

2. Compression

3. Expansion

It is possible to perform this method in a boat or on a surfboard. On a boat, slide the victim's legs and hips under the midship seat. On a surfboard, the rescuer takes a straddle-seated position toward the front end (wider), facing the stern.

When the victim is in a face-up position, there is always danger of aspiration of vomitus, blood or blood clots. This hazard can be reduced by keeping the head extended and turned to one side. If possible, the head should be a little lower than the trunk.

If a second rescuer is available, have him hold the victim's head so that the jaw is jutting out. The helper should be alert to detect the presence of any stomach contents in the mouth and keep the mouth as clean as possible at all times.

BACK-PRESSURE—ARM-LIFT (HOLGER-NIELSEN) METHOD

If there is foreign matter visible in the mouth, wipe it out quickly with your fingers or a cloth wrapped around your fingers.

1. Place the victim face down, bend his elbows and place his hands one upon the other; turn his head slightly to one side and extend it as far as possible, making sure that the chin is jutting out.

FIG. 57.   BACK-PRESSURE—ARM-LIFT METHOD OF RESUSCITATION

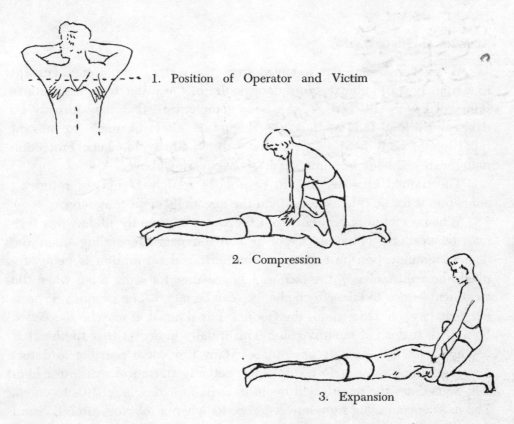

1. Position of Operator and Victim

2. Compression

3. Expansion

2. Kneel at the head of the victim. Place your hands on the flat of the victim's back so that the palms lie just below an imaginary line running between the armpits.
3. Rock forward until the arms are approximately vertical and allow the weight of the upper part of your body to exert steady, even pressure downward upon the hands.
4. Immediately draw his arms upward and toward you, applying enough lift to feel resistance and tension at his shoulders. Then lower the arms to the ground. Repeat this cycle about twelve times per minute, checking the mouth frequently for obstruction.

If a second rescuer is available, have him hold the victim's head so that the jaw continues to jut out. The helper should be alert to detect any stomach contents in the mouth and keep the mouth as clean as possible at all times.

Practice in artificial respiration should be one of the key in-service training activities and should develop within the guards the desire to learn every detail of the lifesaving skill.

ADDITIONAL INFORMATION

Whenever a victim is removed from the water, evaporation (except in extremely warm climates or indoor pools) of the water from the victim's skin will lower, still further, the body temperature that may already be dangerously low. It is at this time that every effort be made to prevent rapid loss of body heat, cover or wrap the victim in blankets. Protection underneath the body is as important as the covering above.

The trained lifeguard should be able to recognize signs of returning animation if for no other reason than the encouragement they offer.

When a victim is brought from the water apparently lifeless, his face may be cyanotic (blue-black) or it may be pale, depending upon the degree of suffocation he endured. While artificial respiration is being applied, the appearance of the face may not change for some time; when the treatment begins to take effect, changes can be noted. The cyanosis, if present, may begin to fade; and if the victim is fair-skinned, it may be succeeded by a distinct flush of healthy color. This usually indicates that the heart is beginning to beat strongly once more. Many times it is possible to detect a strengthening pulse before the victim actually starts to breathe for himself. Sometimes the mouth will begin to twitch, or the finger tips to creep. The most encouraging sign, however, occurs when a sobbing catch is heard during the inspiration of air. This may be followed by a groan and a series of gasping irregular breaths. At this point, the operator should watch carefully to be sure that he is not working against the victim's efforts to breathe for himself. As soon as the victim is breathing somewhat regularly of his own volition, the operator should cease artificial respiration.

In-service training also provides opportunity to develop common understanding as to who does what, when and how, in various rescue situations.

At facilities protected by a one- or two-man staff there is no doubt as to responsibility in rescue situations. The single lifeguard carries the full burden, which may include the removal of an unconscious victim from the water. The properly trained lifeguard will already possess the skills required for a saddleback carry, a fireman's carry and a lift from deep water. He will also know the advantages and disadvantages of each in respect to his strength, the weight of the victim and the facility characteristics (high-sided pool, flush-deck pool, ladders, docks, floats, steep beach, long beach, surf conditions). Common sense and good judgment play an important role here. The lifeguard should not overlook the advisability of soliciting assistance from other persons in removing the victim from the water, in securing and placing a blanket on the pool, deck or beach, in lowering the victim onto the blanket and in summoning a doctor.

Unless an emergency "all-out" or "clear-the-pool" signal has been given prior to the rescue attempt at a "one-guard" facility, it will be necessary for the lifeguard to complete the rescue and removal of the victim from the water and resume his vigilance as quickly as possible.

This problem is lessened somewhat when two guards are on duty and there is a prearranged "cover-up" system (see Chapter 12) in effect. Unless the guard making the rescue gives the "Help-Needed" hand or whistle signal (see Chapter 11) the other lifeguard should continue the surveillance of his own area and the area vacated by the rescuer until he is back at his post again. This is important to remember, especially by inexperienced guards, who may be tempted to leave their post to assist when it is not absolutely necessary.

In larger patrols, with three or more guards, there is usually more opportunity and provision for assisting one another in rescues. This is as it should be, especially in rough waters, the surf, in the use of boats, the use of rescue buoys with attached beach lines and in all cases involving artificial respiration. It is not difficult to comprehend the wisdom and value or preplanning and in-service practice of techniques which result in effective, professional, rather than "clownish" team rescues.

The importance of beginning artificial respiration as soon as possible has been emphasized previously. Teamwork in executing a two-, three-, or four-man carry in removing a victim from the water will permit an uninterrupted continuation of mouth-to-mouth resuscitation which may have been started in the water. If resuscitation efforts include the use of mechanical devices, teamwork helps to insure prompt, methodical action in securing and positioning such equipment. There will also be a smooth transfer from oral to mechanical resuscitation.

Other emergency first-aid skills can be maintained by reviewing material in the original training. Bandaging should be repeated once a week. Practice sessions in the splinting of fractures should emphasize the prevention of additional shock and pain by keeping broken limbs from moving. Practice in the care of minor wounds should also be reviewed and lifeguards should remember to advise recipients of such care that first aid is only temporary (see Wound Care, page 125).

AFTER-CARE OF THE VICTIM

When the victim of a near-drowning is revived, he should not be allowed to get to his feet, get dressed and go home. Until he is breathing regularly, he should be kept covered and remain where he is. If an ambulance arrives, or if for some other reason it is advisable for him to be moved, he should be carried on a stretcher, in an improvised blanket stretcher or in the arms of two or three persons. If he is taken to an emergency room, a hospital or to his home, a doctor should be summoned to check on his condition. Usually, all the revived person requires is warmth and rest. He should not, however, be left alone for some hours, because of the possibility of relapse or of complications setting in.

One who applies artificial respiration must back it with more than the usual amount of patience, courage and fortitude; and his faith in its efficacy should always remain unshaken. He must be prepared to continue its use on a victim long after physical exhaustion prompts him to quit. In the face of almost hopeless conditions, he cannot cease his efforts until there is not one lingering doubt in his mind that the victim is beyond human aid. He should steel himself to face the fact that in many cases all his efforts will not restore life. Even so, he should continue and hope to be rewarded in the end by success. His ears must be sealed to the self-appointed advisers in every crowd that gathers, whose suggestions are hauled out of the remote and dusty recesses of their minds; their suggestions are neither timely nor accurate. It happens now much less frequently than in the past, but there are times when the trained lifesaver must stand by, restrained by some local authority, while less-effective measures, or no efforts at all, are made to revive the victim. This is a burden that has to be borne.

A cool head and a calm, sure precision of movement command the respect of all in an emergency and these are the best assets the lifesaver can possess. There may come a time in the experience of anyone when he must acknowledge that all his effort to revive the victim has been unavailing. Another time may come when his effort is crowned with success and the victim breathes again. Whether successful or unsucessful, the operator can take joy or comfort in the knowledge that, if he did his work skillfully, he has done all that could be done in the best way that the mind of man has yet devised.

Mechanical Methods and Devices

It is neither the purpose nor intent of this Manual to approve or condemn any mechanical equipment available today but rather to provide a simple, layman's description of several devices and an explanation of their use in relation to resuscitation efforts, with and without a manual method previously described.

Now and then, a newspaper account of an asphyxia case and attempts to revive the victim will include an erroneous reference to some mechanical equipment being used. The most common has been "pulmotor." This German invention (1908) pumped oxygen under pressure into the lungs and out under suction. Excessive pressure and suction often ruptured delicate lung tissue (about the consistency of wet tissue paper). The pulmotor, and another device called a Lungmotor (1907) which required a hand-action like a tire pump, were both condemned by the U.S. Bureau of Mines and the U.S. Public Health Service in 1914.

The following terms are most frequently and correctly associated with present-day mechanical devices and adjunct equipment:

INHALATORS

The early models of inhalators contained a gaseous mixture of carbogen (seven percent carbon dioxide and ninety-three percent oxygen). In later models, the percentage was five percent CO_2 and ninety-five percent O_2. At the time, it was felt that the small percentage of carbon dioxide would stimulate the breathing center in the brain. Present-day inhalators usually contain one hundred percent oxygen unless the purchase order or cylinder-refill order specifies otherwise.

Inhalators are not designed to exert positive pressure sufficient to inflate a victim's lungs. Inhalators must, therefore, be used *with* a manual method of artificial respiration. When functioning properly, the inhalator is governed entirely by the respiratory action of the victim. The oxygen is "drawn in" during the inhalation phase of artificial respiration.

The *operating instructions* for most double-cylinder* inhalators include the following:

1. Open one cylinder valve.
2. Open the valve between #1, pressure gauge and the reducing valve. Be sure that the gauge shows pressure.
3. Open the low-pressure regulating valve one complete turn until the breathing bag is inflated, then turn the pointer back to about 10 on the dial.
4. Inflate the face-mask cushion and place the mask over the victim's mouth and nose. (To inflate the cushion, open the screw valve one turn and blow into the tube. Pinch the tube between your fingers and close the screw valve.)
5. Observe the breathing bag for indication of the victim's respiration.
6. As the victim's respiration increases, open the regulating valve to a point where the added flow of oxygen will just keep the breathing bag from collapsing each time the victim inhales.
7. Continue use of inhalator and artificial respiration until the victim's breathing is restored and consciousness is regained.

The factory-setting of the low-pressure regulating valve permits a sufficient flow of oxygen to met the "demand" of the victim. If the demand is greater and the victim's inhalations cause the breathing bag to collapse, the air-inlet valve on the face mask opens automatically, permitting fresh air to complete the inhalations.

As the pressure gauge falls toward zero, it means that the first cylinder is being emptied and that it will be necesary to change to the other "tank." This is done by closing the valve on the first (empty) tank and valve between this tank and the pressure gauge. Then open the similar valves on the opposite side of the inhalator.

The wrenches provided with the inhalator permit easy removal of an empty tank and replacement of a spare. As long as additional full tanks are available, uninterrupted use of the inhalator is assured.

After inhalators have served their purpose they should be cleaned and readied for the next call. Directions for cleaning and maintenance pro-

---

* Small lightweight portable models containing only *one* cylinder are also available and provide oxygen for at least a twenty- to thirty-minute period.

vided by the manufacturer should be followed. The use of any oil or grease is usually *not* recommended.

Replace empty and partially filled cylinders with full tanks before storing the inhalator.

Complete all records or report forms pertaining to the case and use of inhalator.

RESUSCITATORS

The design of these mechanical devices provides for an alternate inflation and deflation of the victim's lungs. Manual artificial respiration is *not* required.

A resuscitator operates by pressure from the oxygen (or carbogen) cylinder and, through a piston-like arrangement, delivers oxygen to the victim through a facepiece at pressures not exceeding four ounces. When the victim's lungs are filled sufficiently to exert a back pressure of four ounces, the piston trips and, by a negative action of about three ounces, expels (sucks) the air from the lungs.

Operating instructions for resuscitators include the following:

1. Place equipment in most convenient position for the operator. This will usually be at the head of the victim.
2. Open equipment case, select proper size face mask and attach to fitting at end of hose.
3. Turn control lever to "Resuscitator."
4. Open flow-control lever full.
5. Open a "tank" valve until gauge shows pressure.
6. Close exhalation valve on face mask or holder.
7. Check operation by placing a hand over the facepiece. If the blockage signal (a fast tripping or clicking sound) is obtained, the machine is working.
8. Place the face mask over the victim's mouth and nose. Maintain an "air-tight" connection. The rubber cushion (inflated) and the proper position of the operator's hands will accomplish this. With the thumbs and first fingers on either side of the mask (holding it in place), the three remaining fingers of each hand can grip the lower jaw and keep the head in the desired extended position.
9. If the equipment is functioning properly, the operator will hear a series of two separate "clicks"—one indicates completion of inhalation; the other indicates completion of exhalation. Completion of both these positive and negative pressure phases is called an in-

terval. A regular rhythm of intervals will continue unless the blockage signal is heard.

Blockage may result from one or more of the following:

a) *foreign bodies* in the breathing passage (gum, chewing tobacco, denture plates, weeds); immediate removal of same is essential. Remove face mask and use the thumb and first finger to pull the foreign body from victim's mouth. A small clasp (forcep-type) can also be used for the same purpose.

b) *liquid material* (mucus, water, blood, clear vomitus). Such materials are best removed by suction. The device included in many resuscitators for this purpose is called an aspirator.

Aspirator—a suction catheter (rubber tubing). Before inserting into the victim's mouth, turn control lever from "Resuscitation" to "Aspiration." Keep the victim's mouth wide open and with the catheter held securely between the first and second fingers insert tip of catheter into the mouth. Move catheter around all areas of the mouth. Do not permit it to attach itself by suction at any one point.

Improvised aspiration can be accomplished by using a rubber syringe. Squeeze the syringe "bulb," forcing all the air from it; insert the tip of the syringe into the victim's mouth and release pressure on the bulb. Repeat as often as is necessary.

When the mechanical aspiration has been completed, remove the catheter; switch control lever back to "Resuscitation"; replace face mask.

c) *tongue blockage.* During unconsciousness it is not unusual for the victim's tongue to drop or fall back in the throat over the air-passage (windpipe). To overcome this blockage it is necessary to pull the tongue forward and keep it there. Although the thumb and first finger can accomplish this, most trained people will use a rubber-tipped tongue clamp, which is furnished with the mechanical equipment. Another good instrument (in the hands of trained people) is an *airway.*

Airway—most resuscitators contain at least two sizes of airways (small for children and large for adults). Open victim's mouth. Gently pull tongue out. Insert airway tip against the roof of the mouth and slide it down. The distance will be determined by the size of the upper palate. The curvature of the airway should follow the contour of the air-passage. The upper end of some airways have a lip or flange. For airways which do not have a lip, it is recommended that a six- to eight-inch length of string or gauze be attached to the upper end, as a precaution. The dangling string outside the victim's mouth and face will indicate that an airway is in use. Once the airway is in place, resuscitation should be resumed.

d) *throat spasm*. A spasm of the vocal cords (laryngeal spasm) is not easily dealt with by the layman. Medical personnel will usually insert a tube beyond or below the vocal cords. The only procedure for the lay person is to keep administering oxygen, to keep the resuscitator working even though a continuous blockage signal is heard. At the same time, if the victim's head is tilted away back and turned slowly from side to side some relaxation of the muscles (vocal cords) may occur and the resuscitation return to normal as indicated by the rhythm of intervals.

Note: As with any mechanical equipment, resuscitators should be inspected or checked regularly to ensure proper operation at all times. Appropriate records regarding use and maintenance should be kept. Cleaning instructions provided by the manufacturer should be followed.

Lifeguard training courses and in-service training sessions should include ample time for instruction and practice in the use of mechanical equipment available. Whenever new or a different type of equipment is obtained, instruction-practice sessions should be scheduled promptly.

General First Aid

With the possible exception of the highly organized, adequately staffed beach patrols, park departments, large municipal departments and some large private, commercial facilities, it is not unusual for lifeguards to be responsible for administering emergency first aid other than resuscitation.

Where there are one or more persons employed or designated specifically as first-aiders, the lifeguard's responsibility ends when the injured patron or member is taken to the first-aid room. To do so, the lifeguard usually must leave his post. A planned, practical "cover-up" system should be in effect, even though the guard may be away from his post for only a short time.

If the lifeguard's on-the-job responsibility includes first aid, there is no substitute for sound basic training. Organizations employing large numbers of lifeguards should either include first-aid training as a pre-requisite for employment and/or include first-aid training in a course for lifeguard candidates.

Do the Right Thing First

In taking care of the victim of any accident, the first step is to size up the situation rapidly but accurately. This will tell you what to do first, and doing the right thing first can be a matter of life or death. Splinting a broken bone is useless if the victim dies within minutes because his breathing has stopped, and artificial respiration won't help a victim who is rapidly bleeding to death. If you have someone to help you, all the really important things can be done almost simultaneously provided you know what needs to be done. Ask yourself these questions:

1. Is he breathing? If not, artificial respiration takes precedence over absolutely everything except the need to control massive bleeding —which you are not likely to miss.

2. Is he bleeding? Rapid loss of blood can cause death in so few minutes that it clearly must be controlled at once. Even less-obvious bleeding can cause shock or death in a relatively short time, so it must be discovered and stopped.

3. Is he in shock? Shock can and does follow almost any type of injury and can cause death even though the initial injury was un-likely to do so.

If none of these problems that demand immediate attention are found, then proceed to examine the victim as thoroughly as possible so as to find all the injuries that he may have sustained. Be extremely gentle and do not move him any more than absolutely necessary in the process of ex-amination or loosening of clothing. Be particularly careful to avoid unneces-sary moving of the head and neck. If the neck happens to be broken, such movement can cause death or permanent paralysis. If any broken bone is found or suspected, immobilize the part before moving the victim.

In general, the victim should be kept lying flat, head level with the body, at least until you are sure of the full extent of his injuries. Unless circumstance demands prompt removal to a safer place, do not move him unless you are sure it is safe to do so or until he can be moved properly by means of a stretcher or suitable substitute.

In everything that you do, remember that *your first duty is not to do harm.* It is better to do nothing than to do something that makes matters

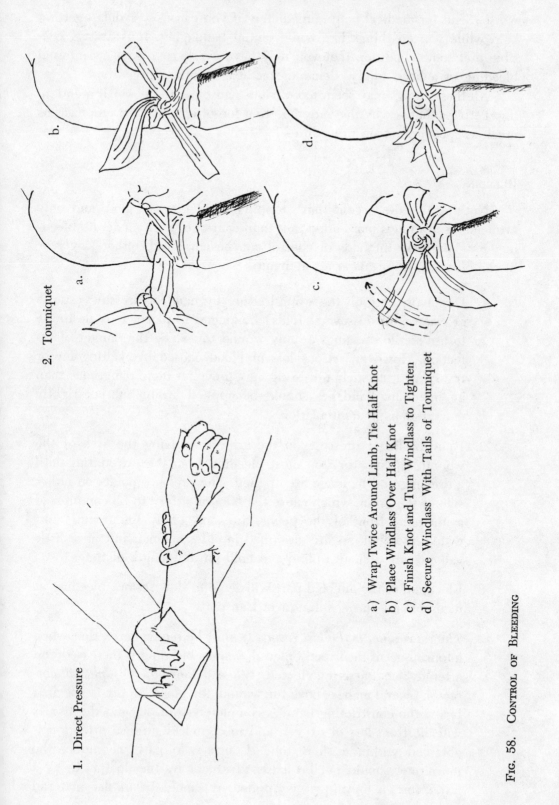

2. Tourniquet

b.

d.

a.

c.

1. Direct Pressure

a) Wrap Twice Around Limb, Tie Half Knot
b) Place Windlass Over Half Knot
c) Finish Knot and Turn Windlass to Tighten
d) Secure Windlass With Tails of Tourniquet

FIG. 58. CONTROL OF BLEEDING

worse. Send for medical help immediately if you can. Never delay getting help while you do things like non-essential bandaging. It is always possible that some condition that you may have overlooked, such as internal bleeding or a head injury, demands medical attention urgently.

All these things may seem too obvious and basic to be worth mentioning. Perhaps that is why they are too often forgotten and need emphasis as much as specific first-aid procedures.

BLEEDING

Nothing is more urgent than stopping rapid loss of blood, and only artificial respiration is more important than control of even moderate bleeding. Four different methods of control can be employed, either singly or in combination, using materials at hand:

1. Direct pressure on the wound either by hand or dressing (sterile or clean cloth in several folds) bandaged in place. It is desirable to use sterile dressings on any wound to reduce the danger of infection. However, serious loss of blood caused by waiting for or transporting to such a dressing may prove far more dangerous than an infection. Bandages should be applied firmly but not tightly enough to hamper circulation.

2. Hand or finger pressure on the artery supplying the area of the wound will slow or stop most bleeding from the extremities until a dressing and bandage are applied. The pressure points on either side of the groin, which cause the femoral artery to be compressed against the front of the pelvis, are most easily found and most widely used. Others are described in older manuals but have little value or are difficult to find and hold for any length of time.

3. Elevation of the affected part will serve to slow serious bleeding at its onset and during subsequent transport.

4. *The tourniquet is the last resort.* It must be remembered that when a tourniquet is incorrectly placed, venous bleeding is increased and arterial bleeding is unaffected. *When a tourniquet is placed correctly*, several inches above the wound, the blood supply to the area below the constricting band is completely shut off, and the tissues will die from loss of oxygen and food, unless surgical attention is obtained within a short time. Contrary to past technique, the tourniquet should not be loosened except by the doctor. If, as a last resort, a tourniquet is applied, it should be of flat material

about two inches wide, tightened till bleeding stops and fixed to continue pressure. The attending physician must be notified that the tourniquet is in place.

SHOCK

All injuries and sudden illness are accompanied by some degree of shock. Shock, the slowing down of all body functions, is oftentimes more serious than the injury itself. Therefore, care must be initiated as soon as possible. Keeping the victim lying down and quiet, and preserving body heat are reasonably simple and also permit other care at the same time.

WOUND CARE

Aside from bleeding control, which has been discussed, it is felt that some general directions for the care of wounds should be mentioned here. A few simple rules, when followed, will greatly reduce the chance of infection and add to the comfort of the victim, as well as making the later medical attention less complicated.

1. When giving first aid to any opening in the skin, the first-aider should have clean, washed hands.
2. Soap and clean water (preferably boiled) may be used to cleanse the area. Care must be exercised to prevent dirt or foreign material from entering the wound.
3. If the wound will receive further care by a physician, it is best that no antiseptic be applied. Consult your doctor concerning antiseptics to be placed in first-aid kits.
4. Cover the wound with a sterile dressing, and bandage in place snugly but not so tightly that circulation is impaired.
5. Even in minor wounds, if signs of infection appear (redness, swelling, pus), bring them to the attention of a physician.

FRACTURES

First aid for fractured bones consists mainly of careful handling (or no handling, unless necessary) so as not to increase the injury. If the victim must be moved or transported other than in an ambulance under expert supervision, the fracture should be immobilized. Using whatever suitable materials are at hand (appropriate length, weight and strength) for splints, apply these in such manner as to keep the broken bone ends from moving and at the same time prevent movement of the adjacent joints. Careful transportation and shock care are a must.

BURNS

First aid for burns is dependent on the degree and the amount of area involved. Burns are classified as:

First Degree—reddening of the skin
Second Degree—blisters
Third Degree—charring or deep destruction of tissues

Pain can be relieved by exclusion of air through the application of many-layered sterile dressings (dry), bandaged in place. Small areas of first or second degree may be well cared for by the careful application of medically approved preparations and sterile dressings.

The commonest type of burn suffered by swimmers is sunburn. Long exposure, both in and out of water, has taken all the pleasure out of many a well-planned and -executed swimming trip. Gradual tanning may be accomplished by initial short exposure time, increased daily until the desired protective pigment layer is built up. Shielding the skin with light clothing, or in some instances the application of shielding lotions or creams, will prevent painful or even serious burns.

Shock care is imperative when large areas of any degree are involved, and shock is generally a threat even when relatively small areas have suffered third-degree burns. Since infection and other complications might be involved, the attention of a physician should be sought.

DIVING INJURIES

Aside from the possibility of a drowning following a diving accident, the most serious consequence can be a broken neck. How such a victim is handled will predetermine his future: life, death, full recovery, permanent disability.

At well-supervised, lifeguard-protected facilities, there is usually little doubt about this kind of water accident. The victim is seen to have struck the diving board, the diving structure, a floating object, another person in the water, or taken a "deep" dive into shallow water.

In any event, great care should be taken in handling such a victim. If neck or back vertebrae are cracked or displaced, even slightly, further displacement may injure the spinal cord, and paralysis or death ensue. The usual lifesaving and shallow water carries are *not* recommended in these cases. The fact that cervical (neck) spine injuries are more prone to result in spinal cord transection than any other vertebrae fractures is indisputable, and emphasizes the need for remembering two basic rules:

1. Always maintain head and neck level with the back.
2. Splint 'em where they float.

The recommended steps and techniques which permit adherence to these rules in handling diving injuries are illustrated on pages 128–29.

In selecting a rigid support, avoid anything that may bend or break. If you have a choice of action, bring the support to the victim, *not* the victim to the support. In rough water and/or in water beyond surf breakers, it is preferable to support, move or float the victim in a position parallel to the waves and swells. Get the rigid support or spineboard under the victim before coming ashore through surf.

Keep in mind, also, that if the victim is unconscious and not breathing, mouth-to-mouth resuscitation can be given as soon as the victim has been placed in a supine (face-up) position. Obviously, this emergency measure will be much less difficult once the rigid support has been placed under the victim.

Additional precautions can also be taken by using other available materials (large beach towels, several regular towels tied together, bathrobe ties, rope, etc.) to encircle the support and victim's body. If only one "tie" is available, encircle the support and body at the chest area; if a second "tie" is available, encircle at the upper thigh area, just below the buttocks. These measures should help to further immobilize the victim's body and to eliminate the possibility of the victim's sliding or rolling off the support in rough water or during the removal from the water.

If no suitable device is immediately available, the victim should be carefully floated into shallow water. As long as the water is not rough and the face is clear to permit breathing, the victim can be supported there quite comfortably until a suitable means of transportation can be obtained. A rigid type stretcher (see Fig. 59) would adequately serve this purpose.

If the diving accident victim is found to be unconscious but breathing, rescuers will probably not encounter difficulty in handling him. If the victim is conscious, however, rescuers should remember that calm, well-selected words of encouragement will have a positive, steadying effect.

Equally as important as proper handling is the need for early medical attention.

Although the described and illustrated techniques are not difficult to perform, it would be well to include them in lifeguard training courses and during in-service training sessions.

FIG. 59. TECHNIQUES FOR IMMEDIATE HANDLING OF DIVING INJURIES

1. If the unconscious victim is found in a prone floating position . . .

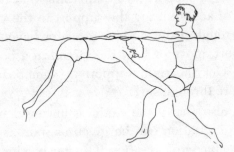

2. Swim to a position beyond the victim's head. While treading water, place one hand on victim's back between the shoulder blades; keep your forearm and upper arm in line with victim's neck and head.

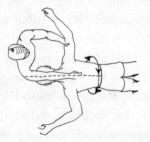

3. Place the other hand (palm up) under the victim's shoulder and grasp the upper arm. Turn (roll) victim *slowly* to a face-up position. Avoid any twisting or flexion of victim's body and neck.

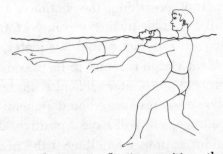

4. With the victim in the supine floating position, the rescuer continues treading water and supporting victim's back, neck and head with the extended arm.
   If a rigid support (spine board) is available, the rescuer should continue step 4 *while the support is floated out and placed under the victim.* The victim can then be moved on the support to shallow water.

5. If it is not possible to place a rigid support under the victim in deep water, it will be necessary to float the victim into shallow water first. This sketch shows the rescuer towing the victim with hand contact at each armpit. Take it easy. Don't rush.

   If the water is not too rough and the rescuer wishes to move the victim toward shore from a side position, one hand should support victim at the center of his back. The rescuer then swims a modified sidestroke toward shore.

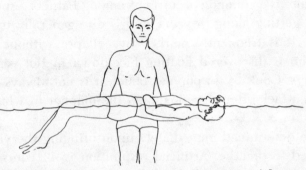

6. After the victim has been moved into shallow water (about waist-deep) take a standing position at his side and fold his arms across his body. Let the water help to support victim. Rescuer keeps victim's body in line by supporting with hands under the back and legs.

   The spine board or other rigid support should then be placed in position under the victim in preparation for removing him from the water. This support is best placed in position by "knifing" it into the water alongside the victim and then carefully floating it up under him.

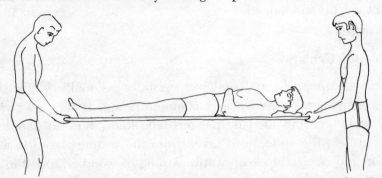

7. Wet, rolled towels or small sandbags should be placed on the "board" alongside victim's neck and head to immobilize these body parts. The victim is now ready for transportation.

HEAD INJURIES

All head injuries resulting from a blow should be regarded as serious whether or not the scalp is split or torn and even if the victim recovers consciousness within a few moments. Often fracture of the skull and concussion of the brain are not recognized immediately and may cause death if the victim is allowed to resume activity. Bleeding from the ears generally indicates fracture at base of skull. The victim should be kept in a reclining position and should not be moved unless absolutely necessary until he has been seen by a doctor. The victim should be kept warm and no stimulants should be given. If the face is normal in color or flushed, the head should be raised; otherwise, it is allowed to remain level.

HEART FAILURE

Heart failure is a common occurrence among bathers, especially among those who are getting along in years, and is due generally to overexertion or excitement. It is frequently marked by collapse without warning and often the victim is discovered floating face-down in the very midst of a group of bathers. Contrary to popular belief, it is not always fatal, but the outcome of an attack often depends upon the manner in which the victim is handled.

It must be determined immediately upon bringing the victim to shore if he has ceased to breathe. Artificial respiration is, of course, resorted to in such a case. If unconscious but still breathing, the victim is placed in a reclining position and covered sufficiently to keep warm. If and when consciousness is restored, the victim should be kept quiet, except in one instance. If he complains that he cannot breathe in the reclining position, he should be propped up; in some forms of heart disease the victim is thus more comfortable. Regardless of the severity of the attack, a physician should always be summoned.

APOPLEXY AND EPILEPSY

Attacks of apoplexy and epilepsy occur occasionally while bathing. Epileptics are generally known in a community and if they go swimming are likely to be accompanied by persons who know how to handle them. In case of attack, the epileptic is taken from the water, placed in a reclining position and covered to keep warm. A plug of wood wrapped in a cloth is inserted between the teeth to prevent the victim from chewing and injuring the tongue.

Apoplexy (stroke) usually attacks persons past fifty years of age and offers as its most characteristic symptoms a flushed and engorged face and neck, and snoring breathing. The victim is placed on his back with head and shoulders raised, covered for warmth and may have cold cloths or ice packs applied to his head. A physician should be summoned.

DIABETES

Diabetes is but one of many medical problems that should be known in an emergency. It has not been uncommon for persons outside the medical profession to mistake *insulin reaction* or *diabetic coma* for alcoholism or drug addiction.

Insulin means life for many diabetics. If too much insulin is taken, or if the regular dose is taken, but less than the usual amount of food is taken the person has an *insulin reaction*. In this condition, the blood sugar level becomes too low. The person may become extremely confused mentally and even unconscious. Insulin reaction frequently occurs suddenly, with little warning, so that the person may not have time or presence of mind to take sugar to prevent it.

If too little insulin is taken over a period of time, or if the person over-eats sweets, the blood sugar level may rise and *diabetic coma* (and unconsciousness) result. This condition may also occur suddenly.

Because either of these conditions may result in death if improperly treated, it is important that diabetics wear a tag on a necklace or bracelet that identifies them and tells what to do in case of a reaction. The Medic-Alert Emblem (bright-red medical insignia known as the caduceus) is a universally recognized identification.

A lifeguard or first aider can quickly check a person's neck or wrist for such identification and should follow the directions given. If the person is conscious he usually can handle the situation alone or can direct others. If identification cannot be found and the person is conscious and can swallow, give him something sweet—candy, sugar or a soft drink. In any event, prompt medical attention is essential.

Injuries From Marine-Life Contact

In contrast to the first-aid problems which are handled by lifeguards at swimming pools and calm, fresh-water facilities, the ocean, or "salt water," guards may be confronted with any number of uncommon types of injuries such as wounds inflicted by marine plants, coral, jellyfish, sting-rays, etc.

It would be virtually impossible to cover all the injuries possible and their care in a manual such as this. Many books, research papers and technical reports available are the products of patient, trying and costly experiments and research compiled by scientists, professional divers and amateurs.

The following information is a general coverage for first aid which may be administered by the lifeguard with subsequent attention by a physician:

Cause: Marine Plants

Prevention: Avoid fast, entangling movements.

First Aid: Move straight up to surface. Look for clear spot. Drop straight down and swim to clear area. Repeat till clear of plant bed.

Cause: Coral

Prevention: Wear shoes, gloves, protective clothing around coral. Avoid contact, be especially careful of surge effects toward coral heads.

Symptoms: Cuts, abrasions, welts, pain and itching. Severe reactions are not usual.

First Aid: Rinse area with baking-soda solution, weak ammonia or plain water. Apply cortisone or antihistamine ointment. Antihistamine may be given by mouth to reduce initial pain and reaction. When initial pain subsides, cleanse the area with soap and water, apply an antiseptic and cover with sterile dressings. Severe cases or those not responding readily should be referred to a physician.

Cause: Sea Urchin

Prevention: Avoid contact. Spines will penetrate most forms of protective covering.

Symptoms: Often immediate and intense burning sensation followed by redness, swelling and aching. Weakness, loss of body sensation, facial swelling and irregular pulse may be noted. Severe cases involving paralysis, respiratory distress and even death have been noted.

First Aid: Remove as many spines as possible with forceps (tweezers, pliers). Cleanse the area and cushion with large, loose dressings. If signs of infection appear, seek medical attention promptly.

Cause: Cone Shells

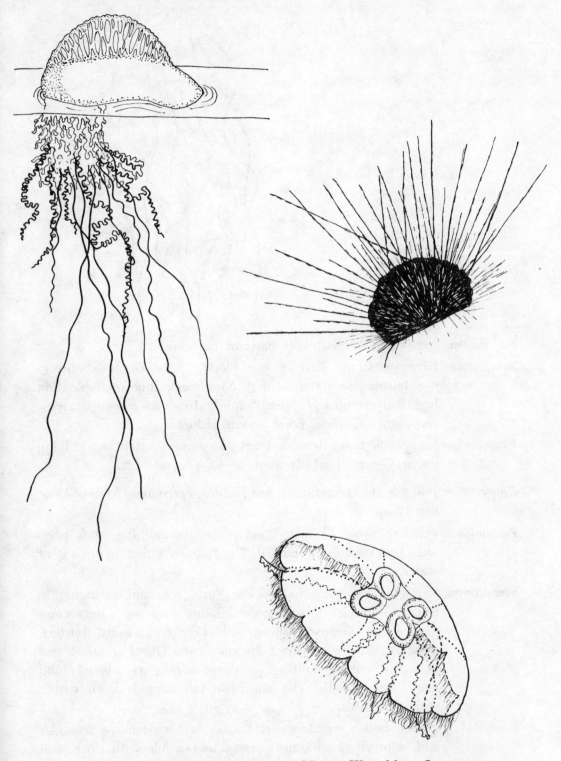

Fig. 60.   Sea Urchin, Portuguese Man-of-War, Moon Jellyfish

FIG. 61. STING JELLYFISH

Prevention: Avoid contact with soft parts of the animal.

Symptoms: Puncture wound. Reduction of blood supply (cyanosis). Stinging, burning sensation at first. Numbness, abnormal sensation
begins at wound and spreads rapidly. In severe cases: paralysis,
respiratory distress, coma, heart failure.

First Aid: No specific care. Remove from water immediately. Keep lying
down. Get medical attention as soon as possible.

Cause: Jellyfish (Coelenterates), Sea Nettles, Portuguese Man-of-War,
Sea Wasp

Prevention: Be alert—avoid contact. Wear protective clothing when present. Avoid whole or partial "dead" parts either in or out of
water.

Symptoms: Variable, according to species. Vary from mild stinging to
intense burning, throbbing or shooting pain; may be accompanied by unconsciousness, reddened skin, welts, blisters,
swelling, skin hemorrhage. In some cases, shock, cramps, loss
of tactile senses, vomiting, paralysis, respiratory difficulty and
convulsions, death. The *sea wasp* has caused death within
several minutes.

First Aid: Obtain buddy assistance and leave water. Remove tentacles
and as much of stinging material as possible with cloth, sea-
weed or sand. Avoid spreading. Apply weak ammonia solu-

FIG. 62.   STINGRAY

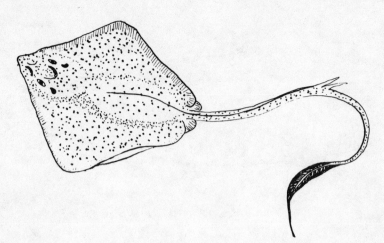

tion, saturated solution of baking soda in water or fresh clean water.

Apply cortisone or antihistamine ointment, anesthetic ointment to relieve pain.

Obtain medical attention as soon as possible in severe cases. If the Portuguese man-of-war or sea wasp is the cause, medical help is essential.

Cause: Octopus

Prevention: Avoid being trapped by tentacles. Porous clothing will hinder action of cups. To prevent bite, avoid mouth area at tentacle origin.

Symptoms: Beak bites (two) produce stinging, swelling, redness and heat. Bleeding out of proportion to size of wound.

First Aid: Apply cold compresses. Keep lying down, feet elevated. Get medical attention as soon as possible if bitten.

No specific care other than bleeding control if profuse.

Cause: Stingrays

Prevention: Avoid stepping on them in shallow water. Avoid contact with barb at base of tail.

Symptoms: Pain within four to ten minutes. Fainting and weakness. Pain increases and may affect entire limb within thirty minutes. Pain maximum in ninety minutes. Wound may be of puncture or laceration type.

First Aid: Remove from water immediately. Wash with sterile saline solution or cold, clean water. Remove remaining portions of barb sheath.

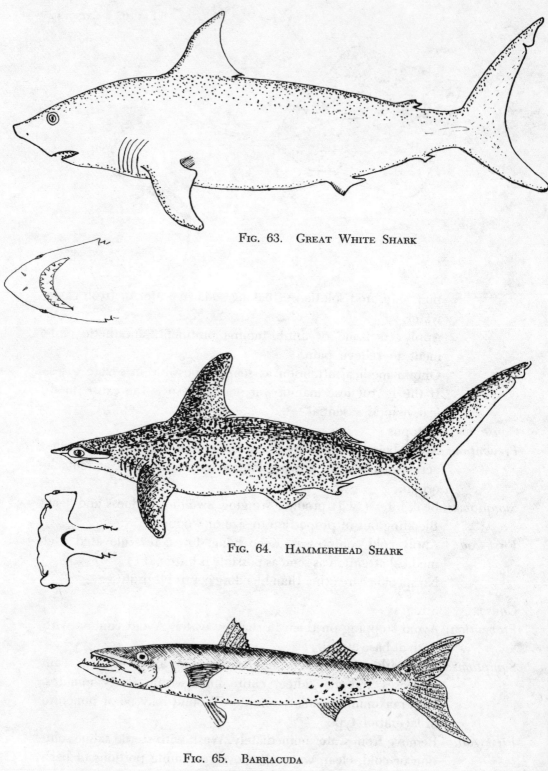

FIG. 63.   GREAT WHITE SHARK

FIG. 64.   HAMMERHEAD SHARK

FIG. 65.   BARRACUDA

Soak in plain hot water for thirty minutes. Hot compresses may be used if soak is not practical. Get medical attention promptly if wound is in chest or abdomen or if symptoms do not subside with heat application.

Cause: Venomous Fish: Horned Sharks, Catfish, Weever Fish, Scorpion Fish, Rabbit Fish, Ratfish, Toadfish, Zebra Fish, Surgeonfish, Stonefish

Prevention: Know swimming area.

Symptoms: Vary with type and contact. Usually of puncture type but may be lacerations. Poison introduced by spines causes redness, swelling, pain, general malaise, muscle spasms, respiratory distress with convulsions and death in severe cases.

First Aid: Three objectives of care are to: (1) alleviate pain, (2) combat effects of venom, (3) prevent secondary infection.

Remove from water immediately. Irrigate with clean, cold water. Make small incision across the wound, apply suction.

Soak in water as hot as can be tolerated (without scalding) for thirty to sixty minutes. Epsom salts added to water may be beneficial.

Cleanse further after soaking. Obtain medical aid as soon as possible.

Cause: Bite Wounds: Shark, Barracuda, Moray Eel, Orca, Others

Prevention: Avoid attracting the predators. Swim quietly while surveying the underwater area. The best prevention is to get out of the water when possibly harmful fish are present.

Symptoms: Serious lacerations from curved bite of shark, straight bite of barracuda and jagged combination of puncture and laceration by moray eel usually cause severe bleeding, loss of tissue and extreme shock.

First Aid: Remove from water immediately. Control serious bleeding by method or methods possible immediately. Treat shock and get medical (surgical) aid as soon as possible. Remember loss of blood can be deadly in a short time, and only immediate control can prevent death.

Cause: Sea Snakes

Prevention: Avoid handling or contact with netted specimens. Their reportedly docile nature may be overrated.

Symptoms: Little local sign at bite area. Toxic signs appear within twenty minutes after bite. Malaise, anxiety, euphoria, muscle spasm, respiratory distress, convulsions, unconsciousness, all signs of shock. Mortality rate twenty-five percent.

First Aid: Leave water immediately. Place restricting band above the bite so as to slow the venous flow to the heart. This is not a tourniquet. Loosen every thirty minutes. Keep victim at complete rest. Get medical aid quickly.

If possible, identify the snake (*it may not be a poisonous type*).

Cause: Eating Contaminated or Poisonous Marine Animals (Too Numerous and Variable to List)

Prevention: Know swimming area.

Symptoms: Variable. Usually start with tingling about lips and tongue, spreading to extremities. Nausea, vomiting, diarrhea and thirst are common. Muscular in-co-ordination, numbness, paralysis and convulsions are not uncommon.

Symptoms may occur any time within thirty hours after eating the fish.

First Aid: Empty the stomach as soon as possible. Large amounts of water (five or six glasses), warm and with salt added, should be swallowed. A touch of the finger on the palate will then usually bring up the stomach contents. More water will aid in cleansing the intestinal tract.

If rash or welts appear, and the victim is able, cool showers may give some relief.

If poisoning is due to eating clams or mussels, baking soda added to the water is beneficial.

Obtain the services of a doctor. Save a small quantity of the fish for analysis and possible aid to medication in severe cases.

First-Aid Supplies

All aquatic facilities should be equipped with a readily accessible first-aid kit. The following supplies are suggested:

- cotton-tipped applicators
- sterile gauze squares (2″ x 2″, 3″ x 3″, 4″ x 4″)
- an antiseptic solution (available under various trade names)
- compresses on adhesive (band-aids, preferably waterproof)
- adhesive tape (assorted widths)
- gauze roller bandages (assorted widths)

- burn dressings
- burn treatment (available under various trade names)
- triangular bandages
- safety pins
- aromatic spirits of ammonia (ampoules and inhalants)
- tweezers
- scissors
- paper drinking cups
- surgical needle (removal of splinters)
- soap
- running water
- bland eye drops one-half to one oz. (bottle with dropper available under various trade names)
- blankets
- stretcher
- splints

It is recommended that these supplies be kept in a clean locker or cabinet, that they be used only for first aid, that adequate accident and first-aid reports be maintained and that depleted supplies be replenished promptly.

A few additional items that serve a useful purpose include:

- a waste receptacle
- an extra chair or two
- a padded table or cot upon which an injured person may sit or recline during first-aid care, to rest awhile, or to await the arrival of a physician if the injury or illness warrants such attention
- a telephone (for emergency use, only)
- an adjacent lavatory

There are other items which could be included in such a listing. What have been listed here are "minimums." Past accident reports and accident potential at the particular facility are factors determining what and how much material and equipment should be in the first-aid room. Monies allocated for same are always a factor.

9

BODY RECOVERY

More than ninety percent of all submerged victims must be brought to the surface within ten minutes of their submersion if they are to have a reasonable chance to survive. Beyond that time, for the most part, the efforts of rescuers will be largely a matter of recovering bodies with little hope of revival. This fact definitely establishes the value of swimming and diving ability under ordinary circumstances, since it is the quickest and most certain manner of getting the victim to the surface.

Recovery of Body by Surface Diving

If the victim goes down even as the rescuer is swimming toward him, no time should be lost. With eyes fixed on the spot where the drowning person was last seen, the rescuer continues to swim and upon reaching that place does a surface dive. Once beneath the surface, the victim is located and the rescuer cuts in behind him. The chin and the hair or nape of the neck are grasped, the rescuer turns and by vigorous leg stroking makes his way to the surface. Back on the surface the victim is shifted into a carry and the rescuer heads for shore.

If the victim disappears beneath the surface before the rescuer arrives or if there is some doubt about the exact spot at which he went down, the trained lifesaver will stop for a moment to survey the situation. First, he must determine the general area in which the victim is supposed to have sunk. Depending upon the distance from shore and the depth of the water, if known, he must plan his course of action. If other persons are present, he should direct them in ways in which they may assist him. This is not time wasted, for meanwhile, if dressed, he may be removing his outer clothing and shoes. Of those gathered at the scene of the accident he may dispatch one to secure and man a rowboat, another may be sent to summon a doctor, a third to get blankets and first-aid equipment and a fourth to locate grappling irons if any are known to be available in the immediate vicinity.

If he has to swim to the area in which he plans to dive, he must take off and move out with an easy stroke, conserving his strength and "wind" for the taxing effort of diving and swimming under water. As he moves into the area in which the victim is supposed to have gone down, he begins to look for telltale bubbles rising to the surface. If there are none and the water is reasonably clear he should swim slowly across the area with his face buried in the water and scan the bottom. Against a dark bottom, the gleam of the arms and legs of the victim can often be detected even at considerable depth. On white sand, the dark color of the hair or the bathing suit indicates the position of the drowned person. When the victim is located in this manner the rescuer does a surface dive, swims down to a position behind the victim and seizes him in the manner previously described. If the bottom is firm, the rescuer places his feet against it and shoves off for the surface. If it is weedy and muddy, the rescuer should swim up.

When the rescuer cannot locate the victim in the foregoing manner either because of general murkiness of the water or because it is after nightfall, a test surface dive is made. If the water is so deep that the rescuer finds it beyond his power to reach bottom, no further attempts should be made. He must then await the arrival of grappling apparatus. If, however, the water is of no great depth he should begin a series of systematic surface dives. Choosing the area he wishes to cover, he should begin to dive at one side and cover the bottom in overlapping lanes across it until the body is located or until he satisfies himself that the victim is not in that section. The dives must be made easily and two or three body-lengths covered along the bottom after each one. The rescuer who strokes along the bottom for a considerable distance may locate the body if he is lucky, but he quickly becomes exhausted by taxing himself in this manner. If he does not recover the victim in the first few attempts, he may be compelled to desist from his efforts long before the given area is completely searched.

Under conditions in which it is impossible to locate the victim by sight, the best procedure is to swim along about six inches above the bottom, sweeping the hands ahead and to the sides in breast-stroke fashion. It is surprising to note how frequently the victim can be located by this systematic groping.

If two or more good divers are present the area can be covered much more quickly and thoroughly if they dive covering the bottom in parallel lines and in formation, rather than haphazardly. When six divers work side by side with lanes slightly overlapping, an area thirty feet in width can be covered in the same time that it takes one diver to cover a five-foot path along the bottom.

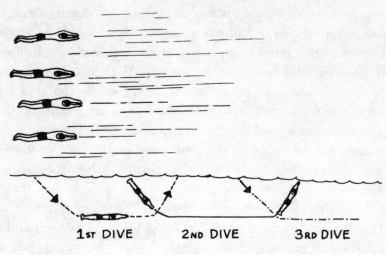

1st DIVE   2nd DIVE   3rd DIVE

FIG. 66.   MASS SURFACE-DIVING FORMATION

This method of rescue or recovery reaches its highest point of effectiveness in the mass-formation surface dive. If large numbers of good swimmers and lifesavers are present when a person is reported missing, they quickly join hands and spread along the beach opposite the swimming area. At a given signal they start walking into the water, searching the bottom with their feet until they reach neck-depth. At that point they start surface diving simultaneously and abreast, taking an agreed-upon number of forward and underwater strokes. After each dive, they come up, move back a body length, realign the group and start the next one, working outward progressively until the victim is located or the entire area covered. In this way tremendous areas may be searched in a surprisingly short time and experience has proved that the victim can be recovered more quickly in this manner than in any other way.

The Water Glass

The water glass, or "water scope," as it is sometimes called, is a device used in clear water to scan the bottom and locate the victim. Even in very clear water, the refraction of light on the surface or the action of waves does not always permit an entirely clear view to the person looking for a victim or an object. To meet this condition, an adaptation of an old device used by sponge divers has been put to use. The sponge diver for many years was accustomed to using a bucket, the bottom of which was knocked out and replaced by a circular piece of glass, and made watertight. Hanging over the side or the stern of his boat, the sponger floated his bucket on the surface and peered into it. Its bottom being below the surface, refraction was eliminated and the diver was able to scan the marine life beneath him and locate sponges.

For the location of a victim on the bottom, the water glass in its present form offers some improvements over the glass-bottomed bucket. In shape, it is not unlike a four-sided megaphone made of wood. The large end, approximately a foot square, is grooved on the inner surface of the four sides about an inch from the edge. In this groove a square of glass is set in whiting or red lead to make it watertight. This four-sided box is eighteen inches high and narrows to an opening at the top approximately three by six inches. This opening is the eye piece and is so designed and shaped that it fits closely about the eyes to keep out light from above as the user looks down. The eye piece is of such width that it excludes the nose to avoid fogging the glass with the breath. A handle or grip is placed on each side, a little lower than midway of the length.

The water glass is used either off a low dock or float, if the object of search is somewhere beneath it, or over the stern of a rowboat if in open water. With the glass end submerged, the user can hold it by means of the handles and scan the bottom either while stationary or while an assistant rows along slowly over the area to be searched.

This piece of apparatus can also be used at night with a powerful flashlight. The light is held above the surface and directed downward outside the water scope. It is not satisfactory to suspend the light within the box, as the reflection upon the glass obscures the vision.

Recovery of Body by Grappling

In only very rare instances has this type of equipment been readily available and used in time to locate and bring a victim to the surface to be resuscitated successfully. The equipment's greatest value and more common use, therefore, has been in the recovery of bodies.

More often than not, this time-consuming, unpleasant task became, and still is, the responsibility of municipal and state police groups wherein the tragedy occurred. Volunteer first-aid, ambulance and rescue squads in many communities also include grappling hooks in their equipment.

In areas where the bottom is weed-grown, dotted with snags and tree stumps or littered with rocks and boulders, the preferred grappling device has been a pole, up to sixteen feet in length, with a large three- to four-inch-span hook secured to one end. With this device, the manipulating action is one of systematic, gentle "probing" rather than a "dragging." At best, it is a blind operation, but practice in its use will enable a person to distinguish between the feeling of rock, wood, weeds and a body.

In grappling operations where the bottom is relatively free of obstructions, another type of device has been preferred. Attempts to obtain information on this subject, based on actual experiences of organized beach patrols, were unsuccessful and happily so. The implication and fact that such groups have had very little or no experience is to their credit—no drownings.

The source of the following information is a municipal police department and is based upon actual experience since 1931 in the tidal waters adjacent to New York City, the Hudson and Hackensack rivers.

The grappling bars used in the Department are simply constructed and easily assembled. (See Figure 59.) The bars are made with three-quarter-inch pipe in lengths varying from two feet to six feet. Starting three inches from the end of the pipe, drill three-sixteenths-inch or one-quarter-inch hole for eye bolt *every six inches*. Drill as many holes as the length of the bar requires. Insert and fasten securely an eye bolt in each hole drilled. Fasten light **S** hook in eye bolt and close that end of **S** hook tight. Then fasten three-inch length of brass or copper sash chain on other part of **S** hook and close tightly so chain will not come off the hook. To the end of each piece of chain fasten another **S** hook (light) to which is fastened a No. 10-0 treble Pfleuger Codfish hook. This hook measures one and one-half inches from center of shaft to point of hook.

At the ends of each pipe or bar fasten an awning fixture as here:

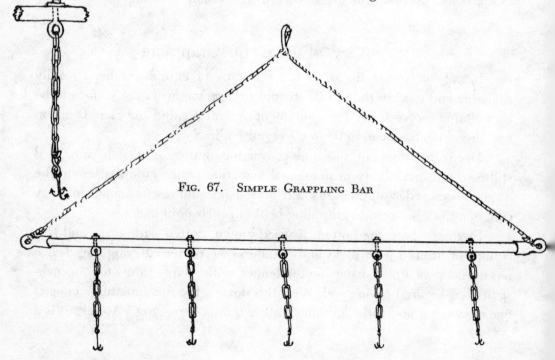

FIG. 67. SIMPLE GRAPPLING BAR

The hole in this fixture makes attaching the ropes a simple matter. Light **S** hooks are suggested so that if the hook should become snarled in some solid object under water from which it cannot be disengaged, an extra strain can be exerted, and **S** hook will open, allowing the loss of only the hook that is caught rather than the entire equipment.

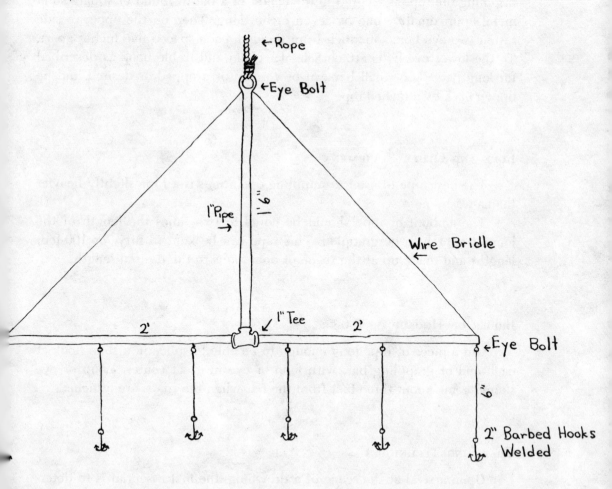

FIG. 68.   ANOTHER TYPE OF GRAPPLING IRON

The length of the bar depends mostly on the type of bottom on which it is to be used. On rather flat, muddy or sandy bottoms the four- or five-foot bar is most suitable. On uneven bottoms the shorter bar should be used else much of the area would be untouched; since the ends of the bar might each be on a high spot, the center area would not be touched by the hooks, or as the bar struck a rise, one end would be high and the other low. Length of chain between bar and hook would depend largely on type of bottom. Never more than six inches of *chain* is sound advice.

Small Grappling Irons

Use in closed areas such as piling, close to dock, etc. An eye bolt for fastening the rope is secured in the center of a bar of round or square solid metal approximately one by seven inches long. Then on the opposite side fasten two eye bolts, one inch from the end, each spaced five inches apart. To the lower eye bolts attach **S** hooks, chain and treble hook as described for long bars. This small bar can be thrown or dropped as desired and be drawn back by attached rope.

Rope and Other Equipment

The best rope to use for grappling operations is a rope slightly heavier than a wash line.

The amount of rope should be equal to two times the length of the longest stretch to be grappled. This rope can be kept in fifty- or 100-foot lengths and made up at the scene of operations to the desired length.

Bridle or Hookup of Bars

Cut a piece of rope long enough to be able to splice in a snap hook at each end of grappling bar, with loop or eye in exact center. Loop or eye should come about three feet from the bar when the snaps are attached.

Grappling Techniques

Upon arrival at the scene of a drowning, the first essential is to determine—by witnesses or by deduction from the facts that are available—as nearly as possible the exact spot at which the victim was last seen. This spot should be marked by buoy or in relation to landmarks. Select the proper-length bar for the type of bottom to be covered and enough rope to cover the area to be grappled.

The most advantageous condition is that in which the body lies between opposite shores of a narrow stream or between docks or piers several hundred feet long.

When ready to start operations of men between piers or docks, rope must be made available to the man on the other side either by rowboat or other means. Both lengths of rope are attached to bridle or grappling bar, each operator having a rope long enough to span the entire distance between operators. The men will station themselves either to the right or to the left of the approximate position of the body. The grappling bar is then lowered to the bottom, and when it has reached the bottom the other operator starts pulling the bar toward him in slow, even pulls, about two or three arm-lengths per five seconds. The bar must not be jerked or pulled fast, as these bars have a tendency to jump and thereby skip some territory that should be covered.

It is important for the operators to remember that a body under water does not weigh very much, and that as soon as additional weight is noticed in pulling the rope, it might be that the hooks have the body and extreme care must be taken thereafter or the body will release itself from the hooks. After additional weight is noticed, pull on rope must be very smooth and slow and bar brought near the surface. If it is found that the body is on the hooks, *do not* raise the body above the surface until it has been secured by rope passed under the arms; it is then lifted from the water. If instead of the body, it is found that debris is on the hook, the operator will clean and untangle the hooks. The operator will then side-step in the direction of the body approximately half the length of the bar, lower it to the bottom at that position and signal the other operator to start pulling. After each drag the man lifting the hooks will side-step in the same direction and the same distance, i.e., one-half the length of the bar, and lower it to the bottom. This method will definitely cover every part of the bottom and should be carried on to approximately 100 or 200 feet (according to conditions) beyond the point at which the victim was last seen. On reaching the outer limit on one end, reverse direction and operators will be covering this area for the second time until they reach the center of operation, when they will cover the area for the first time until they reach the outer limit of the other end. The operators will then work to the center. In this way all the area is covered at least twice, and at the center of operations an area of about twenty feet is covered three times.

It is suggested that all persons expecting to participate in grappling

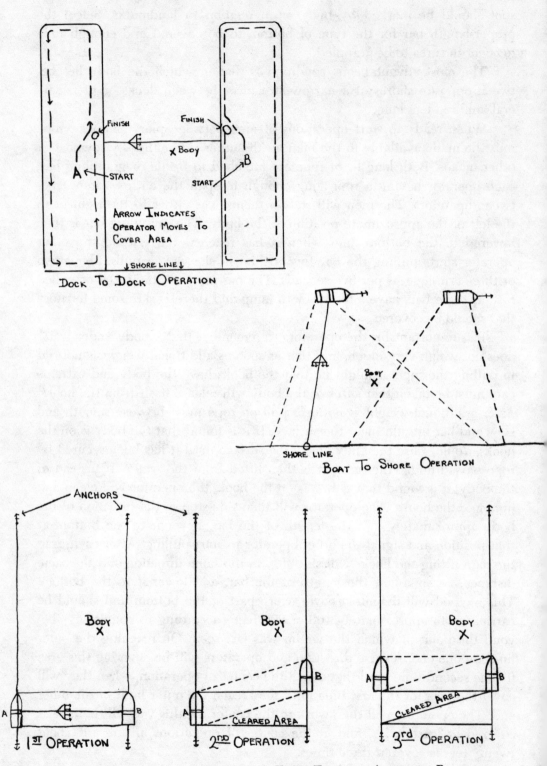

FIG. 69. GRAPPLING OPERATIONS FROM FIXED OR ANCHORED POSITIONS

operations practice a theoretical situation using a burlap bag partly filled to represent the body on the bottom. The future operators will quickly gain the feel of grappling bars and will actually hook the "body."

GRAPPLING FROM SHORE TO ANCHORED BOAT

In this condition it is the operator on shore only that advances the grappling area. This, of course, creates a triangular area to be covered; therefore the anchored boat must be positioned so that the supposed area of the body gets the widest possible coverage. If no results are obtained the anchored boat must be moved enough to cover a new area plus a part of the first area covered.

GRAPPLING BETWEEN ANCHORED BOATS

Each boat is anchored broadside to the other. Enough rope must be used on the anchor ropes to allow entire distance to be covered without lifting the anchors. (Each boat is anchored from both bow and stern.) The boats are moved by pulling on one rope and letting out the other. The operators grapple between boats, each man moving in his boat the distance the bar is to be moved. When the length of the boat has been covered, one of the boats is moved either forward or backward as required, a distance of no more than the length of the boat, and grappling resumes. When this area has been covered, the second boat will move the same distance and same direction and they will be directly opposite each other. Continue these boat movements until sufficient area has been covered. By moving the boats in this manner a large area may be covered even though it involves considerable care and movement.

GRAPPLING FROM A MOVING BOAT

The least advantageous condition for grappling is from a moving boat. The reason is that the movement of a boat is not as perfect a grappling condition as the other methods offer. The movement of the boat must be very slow and the person handling the grappling iron must work from the stern. When there is a tide or current running, it is best to move the boat with the current, as this acts to keep the grappling bar on the bottom. If the tide or current is too fast, the boat should back water so that the movement of the bar is slow. An anchored buoy is used in this type of operation as a reference point. The buoy must be outside the grappling area.

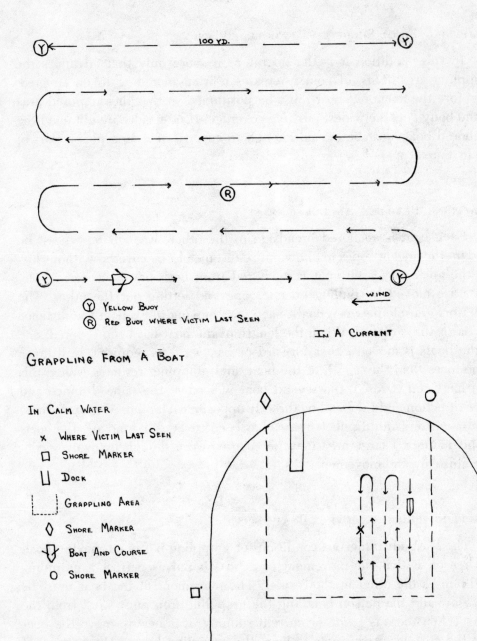

FIG. 70. GRAPPLING OPERATION FROM MOVING BOAT

DROWNED BODIES

When a body sinks below the surface, regardless of the speed of the current, the body will come to rest on the bottom a very short distance from the point of disappearance. It must be remembered that the water at the surfaces moves fastest, and the farther from the surface, the less the speed of the water until at the bottom there is practically no movement of water. While the current on the surface of a river may flow as fast as eight or ten miles per hour, the rate of flow decreases below the surface, being still or nearly still at the bottom. It is a carefully noted fact that regardless of the speed of the tide or current, once the body reaches the bottom it will remain at the spot to which it sank. Of course, there are exceptions to this, but they are extremely rare.

The speed at which a body will sink to the bottom varies according to its construction; a fat person will sink more slowly than a thin person. *In general, the rate of sinking is fast enough so that very little, if any, consideration should be given to the speed of the tide or current when fixing position of a body at the bottom.* The victim will sink faster in fresh water than in salt water.

Bodies will rise to the surface eventually, if not hopelessly entangled, such as underneath a pier or dock that is below the surface of the water. Even murdered bodies with weights attached will sometimes float. Gases of putrefaction (decay) generate from the tissues of the body and distend the skin, which causes the body to float. Putrefaction is faster in sewage-polluted water, etc. In the vicinity of New York City in mid-summer, when the water is warm, bodies come to the surface as quickly as forty-eight hours after they sink. The temperature of the water is an important factor to consider when attempting to estimate when the body will come to the surface. In the winter when the temperature is near freezing, putrefaction is practically stopped and the body will not rise until the water warms enough to allow putrefaction.

In the vicinity of large electric generating plants, it will be found that the water is warmer because of the large amounts of warm water they discharge. It is a definite fact that the waters of Hell Gate are ten degrees warmer than previously, because of the surrounding large electric plants.

Hence, in trying to estimate when a body will float, the following facts must be taken into consideration: the pollution of the water, the temperature of the water, the salinity of the water and the construction of the victim's body (fat or thin). On some occasions, it has been noticed that a violent thunderstorm will hasten a body's rising.

It is important to remember that as soon as a body leaves the bottom on its way to the surface, it is subject to movement by the winds and tides and it may not be discovered when it first comes to the surface. It might be found a considerable distance from the place of drowning.

Putrefaction is faster in the digestive organs; in some cases this might cause the body to rise prematurely and when it arrives at the surface, these gases might escape from the mouth and the rectum and the loss cause the body to sink again. The body will float again when sufficient gases again generate. This time it will remain at the surface until disintegrated.

WHERE TO GRAPPLE

It has been definitely established that in almost all cases, the body will rest on the bottom a short distance from where it was last seen at the surface regardless of tides prevailing in the stream. One known exception to the above occurred in a lake. A good swimmer's body was found approximately 100 feet from where he disappeared from the surface. The place where the body was found was less than five feet in depth. Apparently the victim swam under water, trying to reach the shore after having met with difficulties.

Therefore, it is important to determine as closely as possible from witnesses at the scene, or from available evidence, the exact spot where the victim was last seen. Then when grappling, the area of operations should be at least 100 feet both sides of the established spot of disappearance. This figure may be increased for safety, especially if there is any doubt as to the exact spot of disappearance.

Recovery of Body by Scuba

Although the popularity of skin and scuba diving is increasing rapidly, there are comparatively few who have had actual experience with such equipment in *body recovery* following a drowning. Exceptions to this, of course, are those members of organized diving clubs who have made themselves available to police departments for such purposes, and various municipal and state police units specifically selected, trained and equipped for such emergencies.

The following information represents the experience of an outstanding state police diving unit and is specifically designed for the experienced and qualified diver, who has received professional training in the employment of scuba and other shallow-water diving equipment.

In order to ensure an efficient and safe operation, it is mandatory that one qualified person be designated to direct and co-ordinate all activities at the scene.

Since individuals involved in underwater operations are often exposed to considerable risks, such operations should be carefully planned in accordance with existing problems and experiences at the scene.

What are some of these problems to be considered? How do we cope with them? What method of search do we employ?

Planning the Underwater Operation

1. The following important factors must be considered in planning an underwater operation.

   a) *Characteristics of the water to be searched:*

      (1) *Contamination:* it is recommended that a full face mask be utilized when the water to be searched is known or suspected to be contaminated. The diver's entire body should be fully clothed and protected whenever possible in this type of water.

      (2) *Depth of water:* this factor should serve as a guide as to the number of divers needed for an operation. The deeper the water, the more limitations are placed on the individual diver. Decompression becomes a problem where operations are conducted in waters over thirty feet in depth and reference should be made to the U.S. Navy Standard Decompression Table under these circumstances. It is essential that the location of the nearest decompression station be known prior to operations, for this factor may mean the difference in saving a life, should a diver experience one of the underwater illnesses.

      (3) *Size of area to be searched:* here again is a factor which will determine the number of divers necessary for the underwater operation.

      (4) *Currents and tides:* very often determine the method of underwater search to be employed. In waters where tidal action is experienced, it is recommended that diving operations be restricted to periods of slack tide.

      (5) *Visibility under water:* has a direct bearing on the distance between divers executing the various search patterns. Where visibility is limited, a pair of divers will search side by side and resort to their sense of touch in an attempt to recover a body or object lying on the bottom. A good rule to follow under such

conditions is constantly to maintain *visible* or *physical* contact between divers.

(6) *Ice-covered water:* presents a serious threat to the life of the diver. Under this condition there should be direct contact between the surface and the diver at all times. A life line secured to the diver from the surface is considered good life insurance. It must be remembered that a diver swimming free under water has no sense of direction and could very easily become trapped under the ice, once he loses contact with his searching lines.

b) *Equipment necessary for the operation:*

(1) *Underwater breathing apparatus*

(a) Any one of the following three types of underwater breathing equipment may be utilized effectively, depending upon their limitations and the training of the diver. First, the shallow-water breathing apparatus equipped with connecting hose to a surface air compressor; second, the closed-circuit breathing apparatus (oxygen re-breather) and third, an open-circuit breathing apparatus. This unit consists of a tank containing compressed air, or a mixture of gases, and an air demand regulator, which regulates the air flow equal to that of the surrounding water pressure.

(2) *Air Supply*

(a) The success of a prolonged operation very often depends upon the availability of air-supply sources and necessitates either a portable air compressor or other readily accessible air-supply source, or both. This presents a serious problem in operation where the open-circuit type of breathing apparatus is utilized.

(3) *Surface craft:* certain operations may require the employment of boats.

(4) *Diving suits (wet and dry), swim fins and other personal accessories*

(5) *Lines, buoys and anchors*

c) *Availability of qualified and experienced operational personnel*

d) *Availability of eye witnesses:* witnesses can aid in narrowing down the area to be searched and assist the diver in ascertaining a starting point for operations.

Operations

1. Field headquarters should be established as a base of operations.
   a) A qualified man is assigned to remain at field headquarters to maintain liaison with the operation and other agencies.
   b) All qualified personnel to rendezvous at this point.

2. Scene of operations, both on the shore and in the water, to be protected. (If co-operating with local law-enforcement agency, uniformed officer may be supplied by request.)
   a) Patrol vessels and authorized personnel on the shore should be strategically located surrounding the scene of operations in order to protect the scene from curious boaters, swimmers, divers and other unauthorized spectators who may hamper operations.

3. *Underwater-recovery searching techniques*
   a) *Circling-line technique*
      (1) This type of search is ideal where there is little or no current and the bottom is free of obstacles. It is usually conducted by two divers working as a team.
      (2) *Equipment needed:* 1) "marking line," three-eighths of an inch in diameter, usually sixty feet in length and weighted at one end (length of line may vary and, if possible, be of a pastel color for easier recognition); 2) a "circling line," three-eighths of an inch in diameter and usually fifty feet in length (length of circling lines can be shorter or longer, but at no time longer than the marking line); 3) a "descending line," one-half inch in diameter, length depending on depth of water, heavily weighted at the bottom; 4) a buoy or small rowboat attached to the descending line, buoyant enough to support two divers at the surface.
      (Avoid free descents whenever possible. There is always the ever present danger of becoming lost, hung up on some unknown object or unable to equalize ear pressure.)
      (3) *How conducted:*
         (a) A team of divers (preferably one team consisting of two divers), equipped with a marking line and circling line, make their descent to the bottom via the descending line. At the bottom, one member of the team attaches the circling line to the descending line, making sure it is fastened securely before paying it out to its entire length. The second member works out the marking line alongside the circling

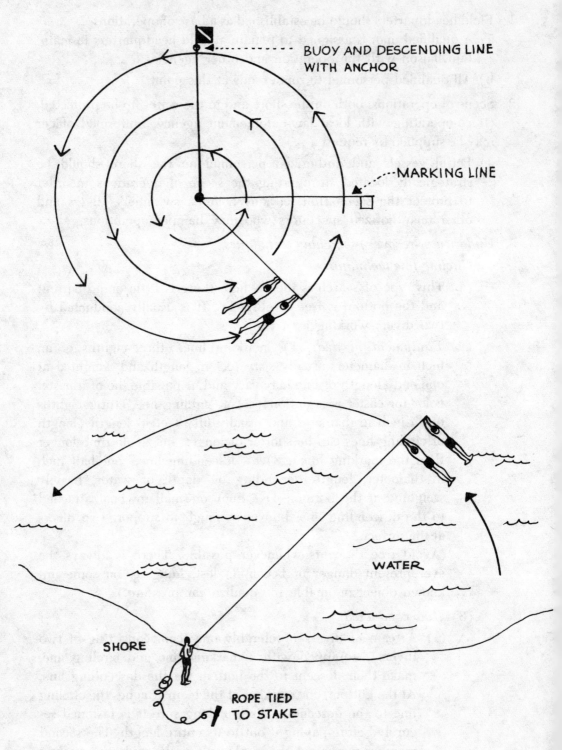

BUOY AND DESCENDING LINE
WITH ANCHOR

MARKING LINE

WATER

SHORE

ROPE TIED
TO STAKE

Fig. 71.   Circle-Line Scuba Search

line until it is fully extended. The team is now prepared to conduct the "circle line search." The search is started from the farthest end of the circling line, by grasping the circling line, as per diagram No. 1, and swimming in a circular orbit, either clockwise or counterclockwise.

(b) If visibility is good, the divers should swim side by side and in sight of each other, off the bottom. Distance maintained between divers will depend upon the visibility. In order to ensure a 360-degree circle, it is important that the inside man maintain at all times a constant tension on the circling line, away from the descending line. The divers should swim free of, but always in sight of, the bottom, for a disturbed bottom will interfere with visibility.

(c) Where the visibility is poor, the divers should swim alongside each other with their near hands interlocked on the circling line and maintain physical contact with the bottom. Both of the diver's arms are extended forward and slightly to each side. This procedure by a team of divers covers an area up to eight feet in one sweep. Upon making one complete sweep, which will be indicated by physical contact with the marking line, both divers move in toward the descending line by two arm lengths, and are now prepared to start their second sweep. This pattern will bring the divers closer to the descending line with each completed sweep and in the event of an emergency the endangered diver may be close enough to utilize this line. The outside man is responsible for gathering in the trailing end of the circling line before commencing the second sweep. This process is continued after each sweep until the entire area within the radius of the circling line is thoroughly searched. Should the circling line become snagged on the bottom, both divers should maintain contact with each other and move in together to check and clear the line. The area searched should be buoyed off in order to avoid searching the same area twice. Then, continue to circle the surrounding area in subsequent search patterns. This procedure will compensate for any margin of error on bearings rendered by eye witnesses. Each subsequent circular search should overlap the previous one by at least one-half the radius of the area searched.

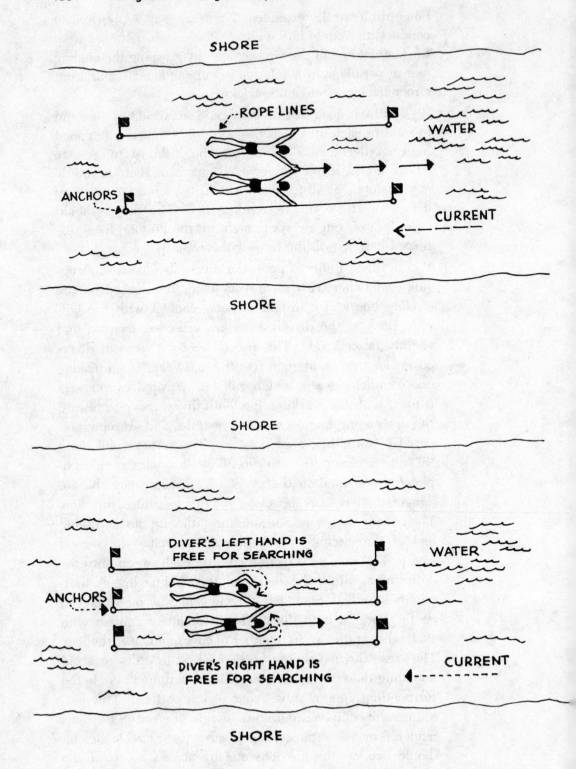

FIG. 72. RUNNING JACK-STAY SCUBA SEARCH

(d) There are several variations of the circle-line search, one of which is the semi-circle search working off the shore line, dock, bulkhead, etc., whatever the case may be.

b) *Running "jack-stay" searching technique*

(1) This type of search is ideal in shallow water (up to fifty feet) or in narrow bodies of water where strong currents are experienced.

(2) *Equipment needed:* two lengths of line, three-eighths of an inch in diameter, one-hundred-foot lengths preferred (lengths will depend on the size and type of area to be searched), four anchors (one for each end of line), four buoys and four "descending lines"; lengths depend upon depth.

(3) *How conducted:* lines are run off either parallel or perpendicular to the shore line, depending upon current or tidal action. The distance between both lines is dependent upon the visibility and the size of object for which the search is being conducted. These lines should be set up by qualified personnel, working from a non-powered boat. The laying of these lines is as important as the divers who actually conduct the search, and particular care and time should be devoted to this phase of the operation. It is recommended that only two divers, working as a team, be utilized in this method of search. Too many divers in the water at the same time invites disaster.

The team of divers descends to the bottom via their respective descending lines. The jack-stay lines should be no farther than five feet apart where visibility is poor. Both divers align themselves on the bottom between the two lines, each holding onto a line with one hand, their near hands interlocked.

If the object being sought is small, it is recommended that the jack-stay lines be no more than four feet apart and the divers align themselves on each side of one line while they conduct the search.

This will allow one hand to be free for probing and feeling purposes. Upon reaching the far end of the jack-stay line, both men will then transfer over to the second line and repeat the same searching technique on the way back.

Upon completing the first sweep, the line nearer the shore, if laid parallel with the shore, is moved to the outermost side of the second line, and anchored the same distance apart as it was in the initial pattern. This procedure is continued until such time as the body or object is located, or the area of search is eliminated.

(4) Three or more parallel jack-stay lines may be utilized in this type of search if desirable, and providing the necessary personnel and equipment are available.

(5) The running jack-stay would be set up from shore line to shore line in narrow bodies of water, such as rivers, streams, canals, etc.

(a) In bodies of water such as these, however, it may be advisable to work the jack-stay lines *against* the current so that maximum visibility can be maintained. In this manner the silt from the disturbed bottom will be carried down current away from the divers.

c) *V pattern (for lakes, ponds and quarries)*

The top man guides the team from the surface, using only masks, fins and snorkel. The center bottom man holds the line. The other divers line up on each side of the center man, each man grasping the harness of the man next to him. It is important to hold this arm stiff and on a 45-degree angle in order to create the V pattern. A set of signals should be predetermined between the top man and the bottom men.

When the divers line up on the surface and are ready to dive, they raise their free hand to signify to the top man that they are ready. The top man then gives the command, *"Divers down!"* The top man leads the team; he does not tow them. All divers surface-dive, maintaining the line in a V and using the free hand to sweep the bottom.

When a bottom man has to leave the line, he reaches over, takes the hand of the man who is holding his harness and places it on the harness of the diver he is holding. He can then surface without breaking the pattern. *This is imperative.*

Be sure that all divers wear two or more pounds of extra weight when on search and recovery. Most searching is done in comparatively shallow water and they will find it extremely difficult to stay comfortably on the bottom without additional weight.

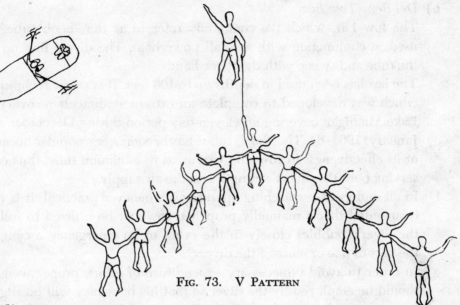

FIG. 73.   V PATTERN

d) *River-cross pattern*

The lead man holds the weighted line, and each of the other divers holds the harness of the man next to him and sweeps the bottom with his free hand. Always move the line of the next sweep downstream, and if the current is strong, place the safety men downstream. A man leaving the line uses the same method as described in section c above.

It is preferable to secure the line to trees or stationary objects on the shoreline whenever possible.

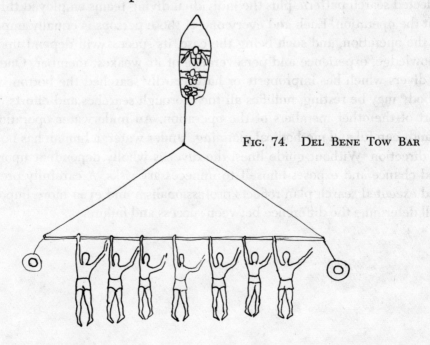

FIG. 74.   DEL BENE TOW BAR

e) *Del Bene Tow Bar*

The tow bar, which we commonly refer to as the "boob tube," is used in conjunction with a small powerboat. The divers line up on the tube and sweep with their free hands.

The bar has been used in depths up to 100 feet. It is a new technique, which was developed to complete an extremely difficult recovery in Lake Michigan covering an eleven-day period during December and January, 1963–64. The "boob tube" has become very popular because of its effectiveness in covering vast areas in minimum time, thus conserving both the divers' strength and the air supply.

f) In all underwater searching operations, whenever practical, it is recommended that a manually propelled rowboat be utilized to follow the diver's bubbles closely in the event of an emergency ascent on the part of one or more of the divers.

g) In order to avoid unnecessary expenditure of effort, proper weights should be employed by the diver so that his buoyancy will be slightly negative when on the bottom. Experience has proved that additional weights will be necessary in waters having strong tides and currents.

Summary

In any of the underwater searching techniques, the success of the search rests upon the shoulders of the persons setting up the lines for the selected search pattern, plus the individual diving teams employed throughout the operation. Each and every one of these persons is equally important to the operation, and such being the case, its success will depend upon the knowledge, experience and perseverance of its weakest member. One team of divers which has improperly or haphazardly searched the bottom where a body may be resting, nullifies all the thorough searches and efforts on the part of the other members of the operation. An underwater operation demands careful and methodical planning. Under water, a human has no sense of direction. Without guide lines, the diver is wholly dependent upon luck and chance and exposes himself to unnecessary risks. A carefully prepared and executed search plan reflects professionalism and even more important, will determine the difference between success and failure.

SECTION III

ADMINISTRATION

ORGANIZATION AND REGULATION OF LIFEGUARDS

10

Size of the Staff

The number of guards in a staff will vary greatly, depending on a number of factors:

1. The physical size and layout of the facility.
2. The number of people using the facility.
3. The total duties of staff members.
4. The financial situation of the organization supporting the staff.

ONE-MAN STAFF

At many small beaches and pools there will be only one guard. If the number of people using the facility is small, this may be adequate; however, there are some disadvantages. There will be poor coverage of the swimming area, especially when a rescue is being made. There will be no coverage for lunch or relief periods. There is likely to be a lack of discipline and over-familiarity with the patrons. On a surf beach one man is not considered adequate or safe under any circumstances.

TWO-MAN STAFF

A two-man staff gives much better protection of the swimming area and allows for lunch and relief periods. One of the guards should definitely be put in charge to avoid development of petty jealousies and disagreements that could adversely affect efficiency.

LARGER PATROLS

It is necessary to have an organized patrol with an administrative leader if there are three or more lifeguards working at one facility. This leader may be variously titled: captain, head or chief guard, supervisor, manager or director. It is his duty to recruit, train, supervise and schedule the life-guards. He will be expected to keep records and make reports. He may also be called upon to do other administrative work connected with the aquatic facilities.

The selection of this person is extremely important. He must have all the skills and knowledge of a good lifeguard plus being able to train and supervise his guards and in many cases deal with the public. He must have the background and maturity to judge people and situations very quickly. He must be able to maintain the respect of his guards and the public.

In the case of large patrols he will have lieutenants or sergeants working under him. However, the overall responsibility for the safety of people using the facilities will be his.

Lifeguard Duties

Following is a list of the responsibilities of a chief guard and his lieutenants as outlined by one of our largest and most successful beach patrols. With slight modifications it would fit almost any situation in beach or pool.

A CHIEF LIFEGUARD SHALL:

1. Schedule lieutenant and lifeguard assignments to cover lunch hours, relief periods, peak coverage for peak loads, sickness or other emergencies, days off, bad weather and drills.

2. Be responsible for the condition and cleanliness of all lifesaving equipment under his jurisdiction.

3. Be responsible for the proper performance of the duties of the lifeguards and lieutenants under his supervision.

4. Recruit and train new guards as needed.

5. Establish the locations of lifeguard stands within his area.

6. Conduct periodic drills of lifeguards in swimming, boating, rescue work, inhalator use and resuscitation sufficient to maintain the lifesaving service at maximum efficiency. Drills covering communications, signals, co-operation and cover-up systems are also important. Each lifeguard must participate in at least one drill per week. Reports on all drills and names of those participating must be submitted to the supervisor. From time to time, a simulated surprise or "alert" drill may also serve to keep the lifeguards on their toes. Good judgment and discretion, as to when and how often this kind of drill is called, is recommended.

7. Check inhalators and/or resuscitators daily, and report his findings, in writing, to the supervisor.

8. Make detailed written reports to the supervisor of all activities and accidents. Make suggestions for future improvements.

9. Designate swimming areas to be used each day and schedule areas for classes or other special groups as needed.

10. Adjust or modify work assignments of lifeguards and lieutenants whenever necessary to ensure maximum work performance and service to the public.

11. Make any necessary reports to the newspapers and generally deal with the public.

A LIEUTENANT LIFEGUARD SHALL:

1. Be responsible to his chief lifeguard and shall carry out within the area to which he is assigned the orders issued to him by his chief.

2. Stay in the area to which he is assigned except in case of emergency.

3. Supervise the lifeguards in the area for which he is responsible, and he shall be responsible for enforcement of "Rules for Lifeguards" and for the faithful and efficient performance of duty by all lifeguards under his supervision.

4. See that the rules and regulations prohibiting ball-playing, peddling, excessive calisthenics and littering are enforced in front of their chair lines in the area to which he is assigned.

5. Make a daily check of condition of all lifesaving equipment in the area for which he is responsible and take such action as may be necessary to remedy any defects he finds in such equipment.

6. When designated, act for the chief in his absence.

LIFEGUARDS

The rules for lifeguard behavior for the most part are similar at beaches and pools. The most important of these are listed by various beaches and pools as follows (they should be adjusted to meet the needs of each aquatic facility). A lifeguard should:

1. Report, ready for duty, in proper uniform a few minutes early, and be in proper position when his shift starts. He should immediately check his equipment to make sure it is in proper place and in good working condition.

2. Be professional, alert, courteous and always tactful.

3. Stay at his assigned post or area except in performance of duty. Maintain an erect and alert position so that he can observe signals from other guards and note anything unusual in the water area he is guarding.

4. Refrain from unnecessary talk or visiting with the public. If talk is necessary, he should do so while keeping assigned area under observation.

5. Make requests and issue orders in a *courteous* and *determined* manner. If orders are not executed in full, and at once, he should report the incident to the head guard or manager.

6. *On stand duty,* take the proper position in the seat. *On walking patrol,* he should concentrate primarily on the water area.

7. Always have a whistle and wear an approved type of identification.

8. Keep people from congregating on walk or beach area in front of the guard stands.

9. Refer detailed inquiries to the head lifeguard or manager.

10. Remove trash or obstruction from the swimming area. He should clear all swimmers out of water during an electrical storm.

11. Not only guard the lives of the patrons but, also, maintain discipline so as to ensure their comfort and pleasure. He should not tolerate any rowdyism.

12. Promptly enforce all facility rules.

13. Keep the facility fit for inspection at all times, keep all litter picked up and keep all lifeguard, lifesaving and first-aid equipment in readiness. He should keep unauthorized personnel and equipment off the guard stand or chair.

14. At the time the facility closes, make a survey of the bottom. He should properly retire stands and stow equipment.

15. Know his specific duties in the event of a major emergency.

16. Check to make certain all doors and gates to facility are locked when a lifeguard is not on duty.

A lifeguard should not:

1. Gather with other guards.

2. Play musical instruments, smoke, read or indulge in by-play.

3. Teach swimming or diving (unless the pool is specifically restricted for instruction, or following clearance with proper authority).

4. Swim unless there is a specified relief for this purpose, except for rescue purposes.

5. Store anything except his own personal belongings in guard room.

6. Leave his post except in case of emergency or when properly relieved.
7. Use lifeguard stands for checking articles of clothing, radios, etc.
8. Use abusive language or profanity in the execution of his duties.

Regulations for Lifeguards on Walking Beach Patrol

1. A walking beach patrol is primarily designed to protect the younger children in shallow water. It is also used as a relief measure from long periods of sitting on a stand. However, you must be alert in response to any emergency while patrolling the beach.

2. First essential is that you patrol at the water's edge, walking so that you are facing the water at about a forty-five-degree angle with the shore line. In this position, your eyes are out on the water—not straight up the beach.

3. An occasional glance toward the beach will catch any ball-playing or rowdyism, which you shall stop without being away from the shore for any length of time.

4. *Be alert for whistles at all times*, particularly the accident signal. You are in a position to move and assist or fill vacancies in towers, etc.

5. On a call from the captain, *run*—do not walk.

6. No loitering while on beach patrol, particularly about the towers; keep moving.

7. The guards on beach patrol should be well spread to all parts of the beach shore line; do not group or go in pairs.

8. Never sit on the sand or lean against any object when on shore duty.

9. Always face the water when on shore duty and assume an alert position; do not watch or participate in games played by the bathers. (Remember, no one ever drowns on the boardwalk.)

10. Do not wear gym shoes when on duty.

11. Be alert at all times. A moment of relaxation may cost a life. Your duty is to protect the bathers; if you feel that you must indulge in fun or flirtation, ask for the day off.

12. Carry your whistle with you at all times.

13. Notify your captain of any accident in nearby areas. *Never leave without captain's knowledge.*

Regulations for Lifeguards on Boat Patrol

1. Boats should be launched and rowed to the patrol area quickly and carefully, avoiding contact with the bathers or swimmers. Do not allow anyone to touch your boat except in an emergency.

2. On busy days and when weather permits, a better job is done when an anchored float is held at your feet in the boat and you are able to stand up at your thwart and watch without drifting. Again, your vision is better from the standing position. The oars are never "shipped" nor is the boat anchored; you simply toss the float overboard as you sit down and get off quickly in any emergency.

3. Do not lean on the gunwale.
   Do not ride the breakers into shore—backwater in on rough days.
   Do not converse with bathers or swimmers.
   Do not leave your area unguarded to chase a beach ball that may be blowing off shore.
   Do not slouch or lie down in the boat; remain seated or standing at the rower's thwart.
   Do not use your anchor to steady your boat unless you are effecting an underwater rescue.

4. All boat exchanges must be made at least fifty feet from the shore line.

5. Always beach your boat stern first.

6. Oars must be shipped when making an exchange.

7. Do not indulge in conversation when making an exchange; speed is necessary.

8. Keep canoes, boats, etc., from public beach and do not allow them within the bathing area.

9. Do not allow bathers to climb into your boat or hang on the gunwale.

10. Do not allow canoes or motorboats within 300 feet of the beach.

11. Bathers on tubes or other artificial floats must be kept within the life lines.

12. Do not leave the boat for more than thirty seconds to cool off; have another guard watch your territory.

13. Each lifeguard must be equipped with a whistle. Never yell or curse at the bathers—use the whistle.

14. During rough weather, all bathers must be sent to the center of the beach.

15. No smoking while on duty.

Some Suggested Rules for the Beach

1. Ball-playing is not allowed.
2. Rowdyism, sand-throwing, etc., is not allowed.
3. Lunches are not to be eaten on the beach.
4. Bottles are not to be taken onto the beach.
5. Dogs are not allowed on the beach.
6. Bicycles are not allowed on the beach.
7. Benches are not to be carried out onto the beach.
8. No blankets as a covering, except when used by one person.
9. Bathers must stay in designated areas.
10. No littering.
11. No scuba gear in the swimming area.
12. No surfboards, boats or canoes in the swimming area.
13. Surf mats in designed areas only.
14. No disrobing in cars or on the beach.
15. Swimmers must stay in designated areas.
16. No one allowed in the water after dark or closing of the beach.
17. No one allowed on the beach after dark.
18. No fishing allowed in or near the swimming areas.
19. No intoxicating drinks allowed on the beach.
20. No peddlers allowed.

Some Suggested Rules for a Pool

1. Running, ball-playing, playing tag, swinging on the ladders and pushing of persons into the pool are strictly prohibited.
2. Do not allow swimmers to splash water on the spectators.
3. Do not allow expectoration in pool or on pool deck.
4. Allow only one person at a time on the diving board.
5. Lifeguards must check pool after each period and before closing.
6. Artificial floating devices are not allowed in the pool.
7. No smoking is allowed in the pool area.
8. All bathers are inspected for cleanliness before entering the pool.
9. Non-swimmers must be kept at the shallow end of the pool. A patron must be able to demonstrate that he or she can swim one length of the pool before being allowed to go up to the deep end of the pool.
10. Swimmers should stay clear of the area in front of the diving board.

Budgets for the Lifeguard Staff

The importance of good long-range budgeting cannot be overemphasized. It should be kept in mind that "A life saved is worth much—a life lost can never be paid for." Budgets should include two major items—salary and equipment.

To have a good lifeguard staff it is necessary to pay good salaries. A good captain, director or manager is worth a great deal. The guards' salaries should keep pace with the local labor market. A system of annual increments should be provided for.

Some lifeguard staffs will work with very simple and limited equipment while others will have a great deal of expensive and complete equipment. The budget should provide for the purchase of new equipment and the repair and maintenance of older equipment.

11

COMMUNICATIONS

The ability to communicate with people and other lifeguards is of primary and vital importance to the person delegated the responsibility of the safety of bathers. Without communications, very little can be done to control people or to prevent accidents in, on or around the water.

There must be communications between the lifeguard and the bathing public. There should be communications between each lifeguard on duty, also between each lifeguard and the headquarters or captain of the lifeguards. There will also have to be a means of communication between the captain or chief of lifeguards and the local Coast Guard, police and first-aid units.

There are three major aspects of communications that lifeguards must consider:

1. To enforce safety rules and regulations in all swimming areas to keep people from getting into dangerous or potentially dangerous situations, areas or current.

2. To control people on the beach or deck in case of emergency or accident.

3. To notify other lifeguards or authorities of emergencies and to summon such assistance as might be needed.

The most important factor in control of people, on the beach or pool, is the ability of the lifeguard to see and to be seen and heard. There should always be a lifeguard stand or chair at each station above the people, so that the guard can be seen and heard as well as see the area. A lifeguard should always be on the stand or chair when the beach is open. This is where people look for help when they are in trouble, or think they are in trouble. If they don't see the lifeguard in his proper place, panic very often results. All types of communication must be simple, clear, direct and easily understood. The cost and maintenance should be reasonable. There are a number of acceptable means of communicating which the lifeguard can use. A description of each follows.

Direct voice: in pools and small bathing areas the use of voice alone is very often sufficient to give safe control of the situation. The voice should be sharp and loud and the directions simple and concise. A small megaphone may be of great assistance in making the voice carry.

Whistle and hand signals: around larger pools and beaches the use of whistle and hand signals are the primary means of communication. The police-type whistle is generally used to call attention to the lifeguard, who then by means of hand signals indicates his directions. It is important to use the whistle sparingly and only when needed. It is like the little boy who cried "Wolf" for fun; when the wolf really did come, no one paid any attention to him. The same thing will happen to the whistle-happy guard. The signals should be simple. Point to the person or persons involved, then clearly motion your directions to them. When communicating with other guards it is important to have a definite whistle code so that there can be no mistakes in your message.

In communications between guards and headquarters, over some distance, or out on the water, the use of a buoy or oar held in various positions will help in making a hand signal more easily understood.

At the end of this chapter there is a suggested set of standardized whistle and hand signals for use by lifeguards.

Flags: flags can be used to mark either safe or unsafe swimming conditions or areas, green for safe and red for unsafe.

On permanently installed flagpoles the green flag should be flying when the beach or pool is open. The red flag should be flying when the beach or pool is closed.

A yellow flag can be used to indicate limited bathing, due to rough surf or bad offshore currents. This type of flag should be a minimum of eighteen by twenty-four inches and should be made of a strong, nonfading material.

Every beach should have a number of portable flagstaffs with red and/or green flags attached. The staffs should be about eight feet long and made so that they can be easily placed around dangerous swimming areas, which bathers should avoid; these flags should be red. Green flags could be used to indicate the limits of the safe bathing areas. The flagstaff should be pointed so that it could be easily planted in the stand. If the area is rocky, a stand should be attached to the staff, which would keep it upright.

Flags are also used on a guard stand to indicate to other guards or headquarters that an emergency situation is present or that a rescue is to be performed and a cover-up system should go into operation. In this case the flag is usually on a staff about four feet long, fixed to the lifeguard stand with a hinge so that it can easily be pushed into a vertical

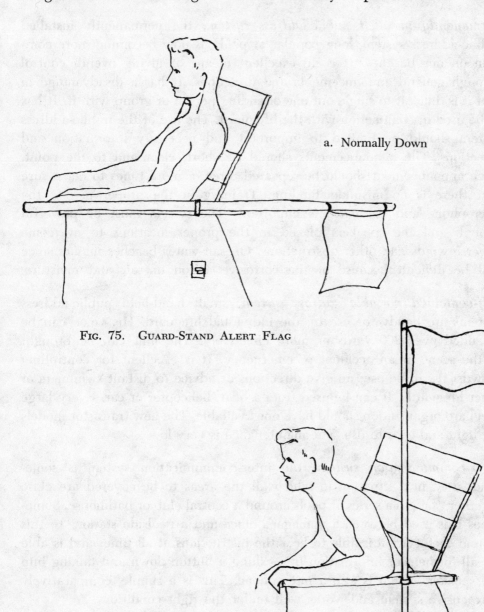

a. Normally Down

FIG. 75. GUARD-STAND ALERT FLAG

b. Raised When on Rescue or Other Emergency Situation

position. It should be kept in a lowered position until the emergency occurs and then by a simple push of the hand the guard raises the flag as he leaves his stand, thus alerting the other guards. The flag should be red and must be easily seen and not obstructed. If it is left flying, it would indicate that that particular section of the beach was closed to swimming.

Permanently installed public-address system: the permanently installed public-address system, long popular at pools, is now becoming more common on our beaches. It is an excellent means of giving overall control through general announcements and directions. It has a disadvantage in that it is difficult to single out one offending person or group with it. It has to be used in conjunction with the lifeguard. The use of the public-address system should be limited to important and necessary information and directions. The announcements should be short, clear and to the point. Each announcement should be repeated three or more times to make sure that there is no misunderstanding. Training in the proper use of the microphone and the voice is important. The system must be powerful enough and the speakers placed in the proper locations to overcome adverse winds and other obstructions. On salt-water beaches maintenance will be difficult because of the corrosive action of salt and moisture.

Self-contained portable address system: small hand-held public-address systems are handy for use by the individual lifeguard. His voice can be extended over 200 yards or more effectively. The unit can be brought to the scene of an accident or emergency. It is excellent for controlling crowds. It can be used to give directions or advice to distant swimmers or other lifeguards. It can be used from a boat, helicopter or car. Every large lifeguard organization should have one available. The new transistor models are light and easy to use. The maintenance is very low.

Inter-communication system: the inter-communication system is sometimes used in a situation in which all the areas to be covered are close together, such as a series of pools around a central club or bathhouse. Sometimes it is used between a manager's office and a poolside station. In this system each station is able to hear the instructions at all times and is able to call for help or information by pushing a button down and talking into the speaker, which is also a microphone. This is a simple, comparatively inexpensive system and works well under the right conditions.

Underwater speakers: there has been some experimentation with the use of underwater speakers to help control bathers in swimming pools. The results are incomplete. However, they do have possibilities.

Telephone system: on larger beaches or aquatic facilities covering large areas, the use of the telephone is of value. There are a number of different systems that could be used. A field 'phone system which uses batteries and a hand crank is one of the simplest forms. In this system, all 'phones can hear the others at all times; therefore, care must be used in identifying the station making the call and the station receiving the call. Each station should have a different number of rings as its call. An emergency call alerting all stations should be established. This is generally three short rings repeated.

The switchboard system is a little more elaborate. It requires a switchboard operator at the headquarters station. Every lifeguard station would be individually connected to the switchboard; the switchboard would be connected to a regular outside telephone. This system is a little more expensive, but has many advantages for a large beach patrol. Each station can be individually contacted or all the stations can be contacted as a group; also direct lines to the Coast Guard, police and first-aid units can be established.

In some instances, a modern push-button 'phone system can be used, which will eliminate a switchboard operator. Occasionally, an ordinary telephone system is used where there are very few stations, widely separated. These could be regular individual telephones with separate numbers or extensions on one 'phone at the headquarters.

For further information contact your local telephone company. The maintenance and repair for telephone communication on the exposed salt-water beaches is extensive because of the corrosive nature of salt and moisture.

Radio: police-type radios are used on some of our larger beach patrols for communicating between lifeguard stands, headquarters and mobile units such as motorboats, jeeps, trucks and helicopters. A large patrol may have its own frequency, but more often it will be part of a city or county police radio network. Permanent radio units should be installed at the headquarters, main guard stands and mobile units.

Battery-powered walkie-talkie radios could be used for other stands or mobile units as necessary. The walkie-talkie radio is extremely handy and useful because it can be taken directly to the scene of the emergency and can give direct firsthand information or receive necessary directions. The modern radio gives excellent service, but the corrosive effect of salt and moisture on our ocean beaches is rough on all electrical equipment. Constant maintenance and repairs are required. A radio-controlled beach is able to be kept in constant contact with every part of its organization, as well as local police and first-aid units; however, when emergencies arise the airways sometimes get jammed with messages and it is difficult to determine what is happening. Every person operating the radio equipment should be thoroughly trained in its operation and know-how to send and receive radio transmissions properly. In some cases, an F.C.C. radio operator's license will be required. The sender and receiver must identify themselves on each transmission, generally by a call letter or number, sometimes by name. All standard messages are given code letters or numbers, so that the air will not be full of long communications. Radio is most effective when used sparingly and properly.

A Suggested Set of Standard Lifeguard Signals

HAND SIGNALS:

1. To indicate a swimmer or other lifeguard
   Point directly at him

2. To indicate a move should be made
   The palm of the hand should be toward the desired position, the arm should be kept as nearly straight as possible and waved in an arc in the desired direction, repeated

FIG. 76. HAND SIGNALS

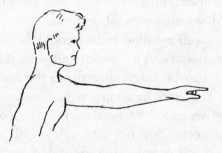

1. Indicating a Swimmer or Guard—Pointing Directly at Him

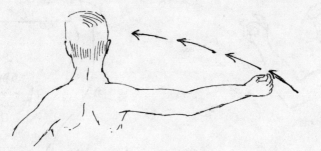

2. Movement Required—Move Arm and Hand With Open Palm in Desired Direction

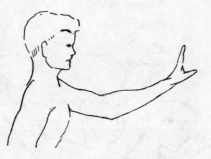

3. Stop or Stay Where You Are—Palm Out—Arm Stationary

a
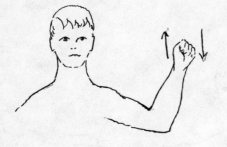

b

4. Help Needed
   a) Clenched Fist Raised Up and Down Over Head
   b) Buoy or Oar Held Vertically and Raised Up and Down

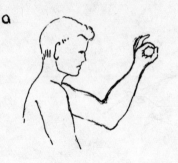

5. Situation Under Control
   a) Thumb and Forefinger Make Circle With Other Three Fingers Extended
   b) Buoy or Oar Held Horizontally

6. Pull on Beach Line—Palm Toward Shore—Wave Hand From Side to Side With Arm Straight

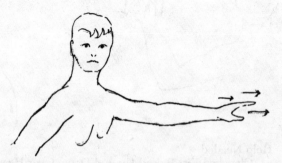

7. Danger Area or Potential Rescue—Three Quick Pointing or Jabbing Motions With Hand, Repeated

3. Stop or stay where you are
   Palm out—held in the universal stop sign

4. Help needed—bring extra buoy or surf line
   a) Clenched fist held over head and moved up and down
   b) Buoy or oar held vertically and moved up and down

5. Situation under control
   a) The O.K. sign—thumb and forefinger make circle—other three fingers extended
   b) A buoy or oar held horizontally

6. Pull on surf line or other line
   Palm toward shore—wave hand from side to side with arm straight

7. Danger area or potential rescue
   Three quick pointing or jabbing actions with the hand, repeated

WHISTLE OR HORN SIGNALS:

1. Attention
   Two long blasts

2. Danger—Rescue—Help Needed
   Three short, sharp blasts, repeated

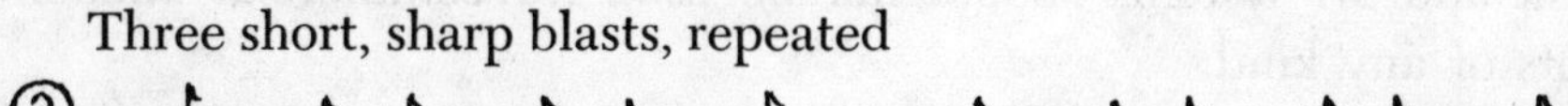

3. Situation under control
   Long, undulating blast—hard, soft, hard, similar to traffic cop's

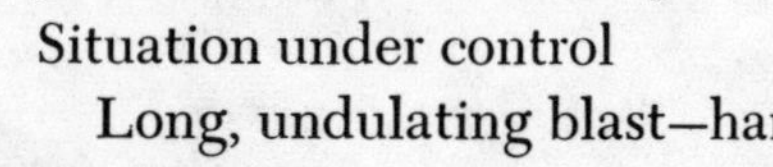

4. First-aid assistance needed
   Four long blasts

5. Police help needed
   Two short blasts, repeated

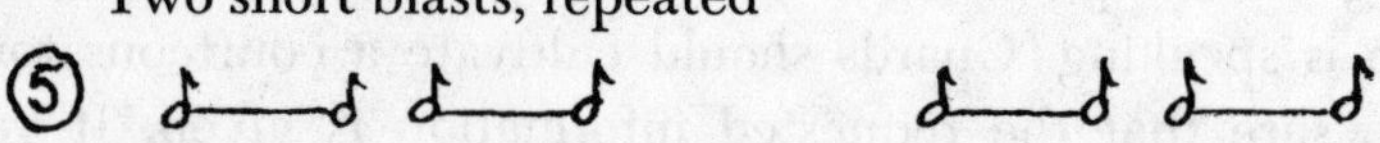

FIG. 77. WHISTLE SIGNALS

Some Good General Rules to Be Observed When Using Electronic Communication Systems

1. The senior guard or captain on duty will be responsible for any abuse of communications equipment, at all times.

2. Any suspension of communication facilities will be reported to headquarters, as soon as possible. Lifeguards are cautioned against attempting to repair or tinker with electrical equipment of any kind, particularly radio, telephone or amplifiers.

PUBLIC-ADDRESS SYSTEMS:

1. In stations or at special events, where public-address systems are being used, guards should be particularly careful what they say and how they speak into microphones. The words "please" and "thank you" take little effort and get a better response.

2. Public-address systems and amplifiers should be used with discretion, and at the direction of the supervising officer. It should not be necessary to alarm a whole area to direct one person. Except in real emergencies, the public should be directed rather than commanded.

3. Public-address systems are to be operated only by lifeguards assigned to the duty.

4. Public-address systems should not be used for commercial announcements of any kind.

TELEPHONE SYSTEMS:

1. Many emergency calls are received over the 'phone. Telephone conversations should be brief to keep lines clear. 'Phones should not be used by the public except in cases of emergency. No personal calls and *no* toll calls, under any conditions, should be made from a station telephone.

2. When answering the telephone, guards should give the name of the station and who is speaking. Guards should cultivate a courteous tone of voice and be sure that the requested information is given. If you don't know the answer, refer the call to headquarters.

RADIO:

1. In installations where police radio is used, guards will be careful to comply with police department regulations for radio communications.

2. All radio communication is to be made, as far as possible, with a standard number code. Conversations will be as brief as possible to transact necessary communication.

   a) Calls will be made, giving the station or unit number, requesting the desired unit number to respond.

   b) Station hearing a call directed to it will respond with the station number or name.

   c) At no time will personal names be used, personal messages or any idle chatter transmitted that has no bearing on the situation.

3. Radio communications are monitored by the Federal Communications Commission. Any violation reported by an agency that indicates disregard of these regulations, abuse or careless handling of radio equipment, will bring immediate disciplinary action. In some cases an F.C.C. limited radio operator will be required.

12

COVER-UP SYSTEMS

It is very important that a cover-up system be established at any pool or beach having two or more lifeguards on duty.

When a lifeguard leaves his stand or position to make a rescue, tend a first-aid case or for other reasons, the areas he is responsible for must be watched by another lifeguard. This cannot be left to chance or a haphazard arrangement. A system must be arranged so that each area is guarded and none left unguarded. One bathing accident will very often tend to panic others in the vicinity and lead to the possibility of one or more additional accidents.

The exact way in which any cover-up system is set up will depend on the location and distances between stands and the number of personnel available.

Every area having bathers must be guarded at all times. When a cover-up system goes into operation each lifeguard not active in the rescue will be responsible for a larger area.

The cover-up system goes into effect upon signal from the stand which signals the rescue, and will follow down the line as needed.

At the beach or pool with only one lifeguard, there is not much that can be done except alert a volunteer or other staff member. If only two lifeguards are present, one of them should stay on shore or deck to guard the whole area, as well as control the crowd and give whatever assistance is needed from the shore line. He should enter the water only if he is absolutely needed. He may move from his normal station to a more advantageous position.

A swimming pool with more than one guard on duty should be divided into overlapping zones to leave relatively small areas unwatched by two or more guards.

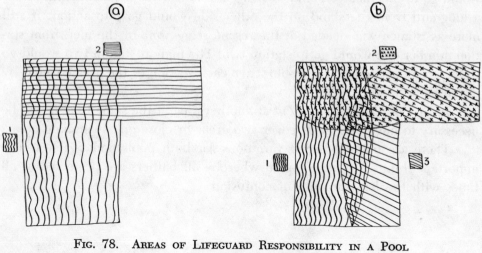

FIG. 78. AREAS OF LIFEGUARD RESPONSIBILITY IN A POOL
a) Two Guards on Duty
b) Three Guards on Duty

The beach or pool having a larger patrol with a number of lifeguard stations or stands should have an extensive cover-up system. On most of the larger patrols there should be two men on each guard stand. One would swim out with the rescue buoy; the other would handle the line or control the crowd, as well as watch the water. A man from the stand on one side

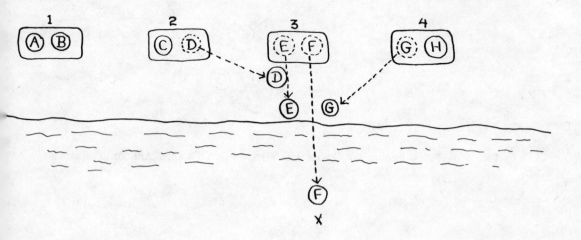

FIG. 79. PLAN PROVIDING COVER UP WHEN THREE GUARDS ARE ON A RESCUE

would go to the vacated stand. If more assistance was needed in the water, a lifeguard from the stand on the other side would go into action. If still more assistance was needed at the rescue scene, one of the men from station number one would go to station two. The man at station two would go to the accident scene. This would leave each section of the area covered by at least one man.

In case of a second accident at another area at the same time it will be necessary to have one stand cover two areas or close one swimming area.

There are many possible variations for both pools and beaches. The important thing is to have a plan whereby all bathers are protected at all times with the least amount of confusion.

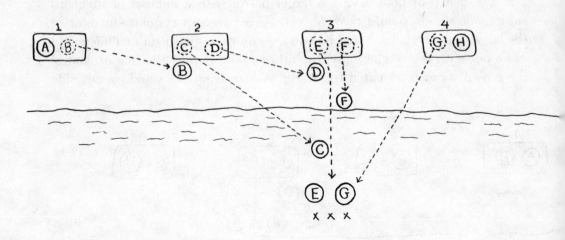

FIG. 80. PLAN PROVIDING COVER UP WHEN FOUR GUARDS ARE ON A RESCUE

13

LEGAL ASPECTS OF LIFEGUARDING

While there are some differences between the various state laws and municipal codes on the subject of the proper legal requirements for effective control of swimming pools and bathing places, the differences are largely of degree and emphasis and not of basic principles of law. While these comments will serve as a guide, it is essential that references be made to state and local law, especially as regards sanitary codes and specific safety devices.

Basic Legal Principles

The owner or operator of a bathing resort or swimming pool is normally required to use what the law calls ordinary, due or reasonable care for the safety of his patrons and to guard them from injury or infection. He must exercise ordinary and reasonable care to provide his patrons with a safe place to swim and must keep his premises in a reasonably safe condition, consistent with all the circumstances and conditions surrounding the particular pool or beach. Any equipment or appliances provided for sanitation, safety or use must be reasonably fit for the purpose for which they are designed and for which they are to be used and must be in reasonably good condition, repair and working order.

The owner or operator of a swimming pool or bathing beach may be called upon in court to defend himself against the allegations of a patron seeking to establish that infectious disease, injury or even death resulted from negligence on the part of the owner, operator or employee of the public bathing facility. In view of the law, therefore, it would appear to be imperative not only that owners and operators familiarize themselves with the legal principles involved but also that supervisory personnel, lifeguards and other employees be instructed thoroughly in their duties and responsibilities.

It should not be imagined that the owner or operator of a swimming pool is the absolute insurer of the safety of his patrons. The mere fact that the patron has been infected or injured or has met his death does not raise what the law calls a presumption of negligence, and it certainly is not any proof of negligence. In other words, the mere fact that any accident or injury happened does not mean that the owner, operator or employee is legally responsible for it. Nor is there legal responsibility simply because the patron developed an infection shortly after he spent an afternoon at the pool. To establish a case, the patron must legally connect the infection with some act of negligence or negligent omission on the part of the pool operator. To the contrary, however, where a swimmer cut his foot on broken glass at the bottom of the pool, the owner was held legally liable on the theory that he had failed in his duty to examine the area for glass or debris and to remove it.

The patron of the pool or beach also has a duty to exercise ordinary care of his own safety. Furthermore, if he has known of a particular danger, or would have known of it by the exercise of ordinary care, or was duly or properly warned of the danger, and he nevertheless placed himself in a perilous and dangerous position, which caused or contributed to his injury or death, he is guilty of what the law calls "contributory negligence." This may cancel out or neutralize any negligence of the owner or operator of the pool.

Question frequently comes up as to whether and to what extent the owner or operator of a pool or beach can limit his liability by posting a "Use at Your Own Risk" or similar sign. These notices generally would appear to be legally ineffective in excusing the owner from responsibility, as contrasted with signs like "Shallow Water, No Diving" which are specific warning signs which the patron disregards at his peril.

Nor would it seem to matter particularly whether the operator charges admission to swim or allows patrons or visitors to swim free of charge. A YMCA which charges a small towel fee would appear to have the same standard of liability and responsibility as an expensive country club. A pool or beach owned and operated by a governmental unit, such as a city, county, township, or school district, is in a somewhat different category, however. The liability of the municipality and of its employees, such as lifeguards and custodians, would seem to depend on whether the courts of the particular state regard the operation of a swimming pool or beach as a *governmental* or a *proprietory* function of the municipality. The traditional view is that the maintenance of a public beach or pool is a governmental activity and that, therefore, the municipality is not legally liable for injuries resulting from the ordinary negligence of its officers, agents or employees. This view would appear to be held most strongly where the facilities are available for public use without charge, or are available upon payment of a very nominal sum insufficient to yield a profit to the governmental unit. The mere fact that the municipality derives some revenue from leasing some portion of the property that includes the bathing facility, for example for a towel concession, restaurant or snack bar, does not change the situation.

On the contrary, however, there is a growing group of states which take the view that even though no charge is made, the operation of the swimming pool or bathing facility by the city, county or school district is not really a governmental function and the municipality is therefore not immune from suit. In California, for example, the non-immunity rule has been adopted by the legislature with the result that many suits have arisen in that state against municipal pool owners and operators. Too, where the municipality makes a profit on the pool or beach operation that is regarded by the court as substantial, the operation is more and more regarded as proprietory and not governmental so that the injured patron is permitted his day in court.

Specific Legal Duties and Responsibilities of Owners, Operators, Supervisors, Lifeguards

The specific duties and responsibilities of the owner or operator of a swimming pool or beach resort and his lifeguards and other employees can be pretty thoroughly set out by analysis of the many cases brought in various courts.

It is fundamental, of course, that adequate supervision and control are essential at all times. This means that there must always be an adequate number of properly trained lifeguards on duty whenever the facility is in use. This personnel must not only be trained and prepared to rescue those who may meet with danger while swimming or bathing but also be alert at all times to act with promptness and competence when the occasion arises. The personnel must make every possible effort to locate those known to be missing and, if required, to rescue and resuscitate the missing person when located. For example, both the operator and lifeguard were held liable in damages for a drowning that occured, in one case, as a result of the in-attentiveness of the lifeguard and, in another case, as a result of the failure of the lifeguard to effect a proper rescue. Furthermore, courts have said that the lifeguard is legally negligent where he failed to rescue a patron who was "in trouble" even though the patron was not yet drowning.

The necessity of close supervision and control is well illustrated by the decisions of several courts holding operators liable for injury to patrons resulting from the boisterous conduct of other patrons. The courts insist it is the duty of the operator and his lifeguards to maintain adequate supervision in order to protect patrons from just such sort of injury. It is not enough simply to post a "No Running" sign; the personnel on duty must use every reasonable effort, including ejecting troublemakers, to enforce the rule or run the risk of being liable in damages for their negligent failure to do their duty.

It is not enough simply to have adequate numbers of personnel. They must be properly trained in techniques of lifeguarding and must be provided with the proper rescue equipment and devices. The equipment must be in good working order and condition, must be available close at hand and the lifeguards must be properly trained in its use. Owners, operators and supervisory personnel must make constant inspections of equipment and must constantly test and examine lifeguards to make certain that they are ready and able to react intelligently and competently to emergencies.

Where the pool or beach has unattended children as patrons (and this is virtually always the case), there is a tendency on the part of the courts to insist that the operator and his supervisors and lifeguards may have a duty to exercise extra special care. In a case where a child who drowned had been permitted to leave the children's wading pool and go into the larger pool without the lifeguard's having made any effort to ascertain whether the child could even swim or having warned the child of the danger of the depth of the larger pool, it was held that there was clearly negligence on the part of both operator and lifeguard.

The lifeguards must be more than "on duty." They must be attentive and wide awake at all times and must remember that they are working and not playing. In one recent drowning case, the operator of the pool was held responsible where testimony produced in court indicated considerable inattention on the part of his lifeguards even though they were well qualified and equipped; the court pointed out in its opinion that "the lifeguards appeared to be devoting excessive attention to certain young lady patrons." Forgetting the business at hand in order to play the he-man can lead to tragic results for all concerned.

The courts have outlined a pretty detailed set of duties with regard to diving boards. As a general rule, it is the duty of the operator to have a reasonably safe board, to install the board over water of a reasonably safe depth and to provide a sufficiently large diving area free from obstruction. Where there are dangerous conditions, specific warnings such as "Shallow Water, Do Not Dive" or "No Diving in This Area" would seem to be indicated as evidence of due care for the safety of patrons.

Proper chemical treatment of the pool is essential, by both operator and supervisory personnel. The sanitary code requirements are, of course, the most obvious reason for ascertaining at all times that disinfectant levels are kept up, that filtration equipment is functioning properly and that algicides and other water control chemicals are employed. However, even though there is no violation of a sanitary code, if there is turbidity or cloudiness of the water, danger of injury is just as great as danger of infection. In one recent case where a patron broke his neck when he dove straight down into three feet of turbid water in the roped-off diving area, the lifeguard and his employer were held to have been negligent in allowing the condition to develop.

Insufficient underwater lights or improper maintenance of lighting equipment, whether by the owner or by the custodian on duty, may also constitute negligence. Where there are insufficient markings to indicate the depth of the water or where the ladders or diving boards are excessively slippery or in disrepair, negligence has also been found by courts.

Judges in various states have found owners, operators, supervisors or lifeguards legally liable for drownings in all of the following situations: where (1) there were insufficient, illegible or missing depth markers; (2) there was a failure to provide a lifeguard; (3) although lifeguards were provided, they were found to be insufficient in number or insufficiently skilled; (4) the operators failed to provide resuscitation equipment or persons skilled in artificial respiration; (5) the lifeguards, although sufficient in number and properly qualified, were inattentive; (6) it was shown that the proper rescue efforts were not undertaken or were not undertaken promptly; (7) there were insufficient or inadequate underwater lights; (8) there was discoloration or turbidity in the water which concealed dangers or hampered location or rescue; (9) the lifeguards failed to prevent boisterous play in the pool; (10) it was shown that the pool sidewalk or ladders were slippery or defective.

Fortunately, the question of responsibility more often involves personal injury rather than death. Courts have repeatedly found the operator or lifeguards liable in these situations, among others: where (1) a diver injures a swimmer by striking him (this is perhaps the most dramatic and common example of the effects of lack of control over the patrons by the lifeguard on duty; these are not cases of a spontaneous leap into the water by a patron but are substantiated by testimony of consistent and continued lack of control by the personnel on duty); (2) there is continued running, pushing and horseplay about the pool (here again, the lifeguard has the affirmative duty of controlling the patrons so that they do not hurt themselves or others); (3) there is a defective ladder or play equipment (here, both the supervisory and custodial personnel must make constant and repeated tests and inspections so that they can prove they have consistently taken all reasonable precautions).

Courts throughout the country are handing down decisions that tend to result in ever-expanding liability and areas of potential liability in the operation of swimming pools and beaches, both private and public. No owner, operator, lifeguard or municipality can be too vigilant in avoiding any of the conditions that may lead to possible injury or death at the beach or pool. A swimming facility naturally lends itself to situations that can result in injury or drowning. It is to be expected in the years ahead that more cases will arise involving horseplay; unsupervised games in the water or the walk areas; spread of contagious disease or excessive turbidity in pools where proper chemical treatment is not provided; eye injury caused by excessive chlorination; infection caused by common use of bathing suits or towels; and a dozen other things. In all these cases the owners, operators and lifeguards will be required to show that they have performed their jobs in a competent and proper fashion without any negligence or omission. If the utmost care is taken by each person connected with the operation of the facility, the number of incidents will be greatly reduced and those that do happen will be truly accidents, for which the personnel are not legally responsible.

What to Do When an Incident Occurs

It should be made clear that every incident, whether apparently serious or trivial, may be the basis for a lawsuit against the owner, supervisor or lifeguard, or all of them. The courts are open to all, and anyone may start a lawsuit against anybody at any time. It is essential that all personnel involved proceed with these possibilities in mind.

From time to time there are situations in which, because of the severity of the submersion of accident, the police, emergency squad or hospital ambulance may be required. It is a crucial part of the lifeguard's duty in submersion cases to continue artificial respiration or to use the resuscitation equipment until the crisis has passed or the police or emergency personnel have arrived and taken charge. No lifeguard should ever assume the responsibility of deciding that rescue efforts are useless. The lifeguard should continue treatment without pause unless and until a qualified doctor or the police squad relieves him. The lifeguard is obligated, as a part of his duty, to continue to render any assistance that the police or emergency squad may require of him. If a hospital doctor arrives with the ambulance or a doctor arrives on the scene, the lifeguard should continue to administer treatment under the direction of the doctor, who immediately assumes legal responsibility for the case. The doctor will determine whether further treatment is of no avail or is not necessary. It is the doctor who will pronounce the victim dead or instruct the lifeguard to discontinue treatment; his decision is the legal and final one and it must be accepted by the lifeguard and his supervisors without dispute.

In accident cases not involving submersion, such as falls, cuts and the like, the same rules of conduct apply. The lifeguard must at all times be reminded that he has been trained for just these emergencies; yet he must unquestionably defer to medical and police treatment.

In any incident at the pool or beach, the lifeguard and his supervisors should assume the worst from a legal point of view. It is always best to be prepared for the inevitable barrage of questions, especially from news media, and for the possible lawsuit that may result from the incident. The lifeguard and the operator should not attempt, by word or deed, to prejudge either the legal responsibility for the incident or its seriousness. In all cases involving any claim of injury or in any submersion case no matter how trivial it may seem and no matter how much the victim may protest that "I'm all right," "It isn't serious," "Don't worry" or the like, the lifeguard should, at the very first opportunity, make a complete written report to the designated supervisor of the facility. This report should be complete, factual and detailed and should be transmitted promptly to the owners or managers. The lifeguard should never assume that the information is known to his supervisors.

In cases in which there has obviously been a serious injury, in all cases involving the use of rescue and resuscitation equipment or where the police or ambulance squad were summoned, it is suggested that an informal hearing be conducted as soon as possible after the incident so that all relevant information can be obtained and gathered. It is suggested that the testimony and statements should be transcribed stenographically and that the owner or person in charge of the facility should be present. This written report and transcription will be invaluable in providing a defense based on fact, freshly recalled after the incident, if a claim or lawsuit does result.

The following outline is a suggested list of questions which can be altered to fit the particular circumstances of the case and will serve as a general guide setting forth the information required in the report or at the informal hearing.

Information Required in Injury or Submersion Cases

1. Names, titles, employment history and location of assignment of all employees involved.

2. Date, type and amount of training and experience in lifeguarding and first-aid techniques of all employees involved.

3. Time and location of injury or submersion.

4. Names, addresses, ages of person or persons involved in injury or submersion.

5. Description of water and weather temperatures and conditions at the time of the incident.

6. Population load of beach or pool at time of incident.

7. How did involved employee or employees first became aware of incident? Exact time is essential.

8. What were initial steps of employee or employees involved? How much time elapsed between incident and first action?

9. (In rescue cases only)

   a) How far did employee have to swim?
   b) Did rescuing employee have any assistance?
   c) Were there any impediments to the rescue?
   d) How much time elapsed before rescue?
   e) Was any equipment (boat, buoy, etc.) used in rescue?
   f) What steps (if required) were taken for reviving the victim?
   g) Was artificial respiration required? If so, give names of persons applying it, length of time employed and description of methods used.
   h) Was resuscitation or other equipment used?

      (1) Describe equipment used.
      (2) Was it readily available or did it have to be brought to the scene?
      (3) Was equipment in good working order? If not, describe deficiencies.
      (4) How long was it used?

10. Was the injured person or victim identified? By whom?

11. What was the cause of the injury or submersion?

    a) What was the victim doing at the time of the injury or submersion?
    b) Could the victim swim? State degree of proficiency.
    c) Did the victim disregard any of the rules of the pool or beach or any specific orders of the lifeguard? If so, describe in detail.

12. Were the police, emergency or ambulance squad or doctors called? (If applicable)

   a) Who called them?
   b) How soon did they respond?
   c) What action did they take?
   d) Was first aid given? (If applicable) If so, by whom?
   e) Was artificial respiration or resuscitation given or continued? If so, by whom and for how long?
   f) Did a doctor arrive on the scene? If so, did he assume control? When?
   g) Did a doctor make any declaration as to the victim's condition?
   h) Was the victim removed from the beach or pool area? If so, by whom and under what conditions?

13. Please make any additional general comments you think may be relevant or pertinent that were not covered in the specific questions.

14. If it is pertinent or relevant, please prepare a sketch of the area involved in the injury or incident.

14

RECORDS AND REPORTS

Safety is acknowledged as the primary concern of all aquatic personnel and especially of the lifeguards, who are trained in lifesaving and accident prevention. Secondary, but very important, is the keeping of daily records and reports for the efficient operation and maintenance of bathing areas and adherence to safe procedures which will assist in preventive measures. A thorough working knowledge of an area of responsibility can be obtained through records and reports and will establish standards that will maintain safe procedures.

Pools

State public health bureaus or departments will dictate standards and practices regarding health, sanitation and management of swimming pools. However, each of the following recommended items should be incorporated in a standard record form and each item should be studied to see how it can be handled locally to the best advantage.

1. Considerations to include:

    a) Water supply
        (1) Treatment, analysis, bacteria count

    b) Time of inspection
        (1) Peak use
        (2) Minimum use
        (3) Frequency

    c) Pool structure
        (1) Physical condition

d) Supplemental facilities

   (1) Refuse

   (2) Drinking fountains

   (3) Emergency and rescue equipment

e) Filtration system

   (1) Adequacy

   (2) Maintenance

f) Buildings, spectator galleries, enclosures

   (1) Ventilation, lighting

   (2) Plumbing and drainage maintenance

   (3) Surroundings

g) Water condition

   (1) CH_2 and PH level

   (2) Turbidity

   (3) Peak load

   (4) Varied: hours of day and days of week

h) Showers, toilets, dressing rooms

   (1) Cleanliness

   (2) Towels, soap, hot water

i) Bather control

   (1) Pool capacity

   (2) Guard duty and area

2. Daily records will include:

a) Date

b) Time of test

c) Turbidity

d) Free available chlorine at inlet, outlet (taken at two different times)

e) Alkalinity at inlet, outlet

    f) Amount of disinfectant added

    g) Hours of pool operation

    h) Water and room temperature

    i) Alum and soda ash added

    j) Fresh water added

Beaches

1. Captain's daily log

    a) Personnel on duty

    b) Weather and water conditions

    c) Number of people using beach

    d) Number and type of rescues

    e) Number and type of first-aid cases

    f) Equipment report

2. Lifeguard report

    a) On duty

    b) Subject accident report

    c) Number and type of rescues, police actions, first-aid treatments:
        (1) Name, address, telephone, age, sex, occupation
        (2) Cause of action, condition of subject on release
        (3) Witnesses' names and addresses
        (4) Disposition of case—doctor, hospital
        (5) Time of action and date
        (6) Action taken

    d) Equipment report—lost, damaged

    e) Unusual incidents

Note: One aspect of records and reports that cannot be overemphasized is the necessity and importance of adequate data (accurate details) pertaining to accidents and drownings. These are invaluable in any subsequent lawsuit.

APPENDIX

SUGGESTED COURSE OUTLINE
FOR TRAINING LIFEGUARDS
ON SURF BEACHES

(Project of CNCA Committee On Lifeguard Training)

I. Prerequisities—Chapter 1

    A. Age eighteen years—male or female
       (Males preferred for large open-water beaches.)

    B. Physical examination

    C. Ability to swim 440 yards in open water in twelve minutes

    D. Holder of a current Red Cross or YMCA Senior Lifesaving certificate or its equivalent

    E. Supplies references attesting to maturity and judgment, reliability and character

II. Course Outline

    A. Guarding on Surf Beaches (Lecture), Time—1 hour

    B. Waves and Surf Conditions (Lecture), Time—1 hour

    C. Organization and Administration (Lecture), Time—2 hours

    D. First Aid on the Beach (Lecture), Time—3 hours (in addition to 10-hour Standard First Aid Course)

    E. Swimming Rescues in Surf (Practical Water Work), Time—5 hours
       DEPENDING ON LOCAL USE AND NEED, ONE OR MORE OF THE FOLLOWING:

    F. Surfboat Rescues (Practical Work in Water), Time—5 hours

    G. Surfboard Rescues (Practical Water Work), Time—5 hours

    H. Other Specialized Rescue Methods (Practical Water Work), Time—5 hours (or as needed)

A. Guarding on Surf Beaches

   1. Your primary job is to prevent accidents. Your secondary job is to make rescues if necessary. (Chapter 1)

   2. Know yourself. Know your beach. Know how to keep people out of danger. Know how to get to your victim. Know what to do with your victim.

   3. Preventive lifeguarding—Surf (Chapter 3)

      a. Eyes

         (1) nonswimmers
         (2) tired or weak swimmers
         (3) tubes
         (4) mats
         (5) groups
            (a) loving couples
            (b) groups playing games

      b. Dry land guarding

         (1) Keep people out of trouble before they get into it.
         (2) Keep bathers out of dangerous current situations.
         (3) Use of whistles and flags.

      c. Importance of equipment and use: Always use equipment in surf rescues.

      d. Control of people on beach

         (1) around guard stand
         (2) around boat or board
         (3) around scene of accident

B. Waves and Surf Conditions (Chapter 4)

   1. Surf

      a. Waves

         (1) motion of water in a wave
         (2) shape and type of waves
         (3) direction of waves
         (4) how to swim in waves

      b. Currents
         (1) undertow

(2) run out, seapuss or offshore current
(3) set
(4) sloughs—finger rips
(5) set off or hole

c. Tides

d. Bars

e. Wind

(1) effects on surf
(2) danger of wind shifts

f. Obstructions: Stay away.

g. Surf Indicators

(1) light-colored water	—shallow
(2) dark-colored water	—deep
(3) breaking waves	—shallow
(4) rolling waves	—deep
(5) short steep beach	—strong undertow
(6) long easy beach	—weak undertow
(7) choppy water	—onshore or quartering wind
(8) smooth water	—offshore wind
(9) rolling beach	—watch for sloughs and run outs
(10) choppy water in one place—look for run out	

C. Organization and Maintenance of the Beach Patrol (Chapter 10)

1. Size of the patrol
   (Depends on the situation.)

2. Organization of the patrol

   a. one-man patrol
   b. two-man patrol
   c. three-man patrol
   d. larger patrols

3. Cooperation and signals between guards and stands (Chapters 11–12)

   a. A system of covering up must be developed to fit the need.
   b. Signals which are simple and understandable should be used.
   c. If large distances are involved the use of flags, telephones and radio is advisable.

4. Schedules (Chapter 10)

5. Drills (Chapter 2)

    a. regular and surprise
    b. the importance of drills

6. The importance of good budgets (Chapter 10)

    a. pay scales: Keep in mind that a life saved is worth much, one life lost cannot be paid for.
    b. for equipment

7. Equipment (Chapter 5)

    a. patrol equipment

        (1) buoys
        (2) beach lines
        (3) boats
        (4) oars
        (5) boards
        (6) belts
        (7) guard stands or towers
        (8) danger flags and signs
        (9) ropes to mark areas
     (10) first-aid kits (Chapter 8)

    b. personal equipment, uniforms

        (1) whistle
        (2) hat
        (3) sunglasses
        (4) bathing suit
        (5) jacket
        (6) badge

8. Reports and records (Chapter 14)

    a. captain's daily log
    b. stand or tower report

9. Legal problems (have a lawyers' advice—Chapter 13)

    a. Captain or men should be special police officers.
    b. Cooperation of and with police is a necessity.
    c. Cooperation of the Coast Guard is a necessity.
    d. cooperation of other municipal authorities

    e. rules and regulations: Local ordinances should be obtained to control the conduct of the bathing public for their safety.

    f. importance of reports and records

    g. lifeguards' liability

D. First Aid on the Beach (Chapter 8)

  1. First period

    a. wounds
    b. fish hooks
    c. injuries from marine life contact
    d. sunburn
    e. sand in eyes
    f. exhaustion

  2. Second period

  (drowning and artificial respiration)

  3. Third period

    a. broken limbs
    b. broken back and neck
    c. care of shock

E. Swimming Rescues in Surf (Chapter 7)

  1. First period—without equipment

    a. approaches
    b. tows

  2. Second period—with free torpedo or can buoy (Chapter 6)

    a. description of buoys
      (advantage and disadvantage)
    b. securing buoy
    c. entry into water
    d. approaches
    e. Tell victim how to hold onto can.
    f. swimming with buoy and victim

  3. Third period—torpedo or can buoy with beach line attached

    a. approaches
    b. placing victim on buoy
    c. group needing rescue

d. unconscious victim

e. handling line on beach

4. Improvised equipment

a. towels, other extensions

b. balls

c. mats, etc.

d. other equipment

5. Test

a. Free swimming rescues

(1) rescue of unconscious victims using cross chest carry (100 ft.)

(2) Rescue using blocks and carry or wrist tow (50 yds.)

(3) Rescue with struggling victim (100 ft.)

b. equipment rescues

(1) free torpedo buoys rescue conscious victim (100 yds.)

(2) can and beach line rescue of two victims 20 feet apart (100 yds.)

(3) Belt and line rescue struggling victim (50 yds.)

F. Surfboat Rescues (Chapter 6)

1. General information on handling boats in the surf

2. Launching and trim of boat

3. Rowing to seaward

(use of currents and lulls)

4. Rowing to shore and landing

a. stern first

b. bow first

5. Rescues

a. extensions and support

b. over the side

c. over the stern

d. fend off

e. artificial respiration

6. Riding the wave in

G. Surfboard Rescues (Chapter 6)

  1. General information on handling surfboards in the surf

  2. Launch and trim of surfboard

  3. Paddling out through the surf

      a. trim
      b. how to go through or over waves
      c. how to use currents and lulls

  4. Paddling back to shore

      a. trim with and without victim
      b. holding victim on board
      c. breaking waves

  5. Rescues

      a. tired swimmer
      b. unconscious or helpless victim
      c. group support
      d. fend off

  6. Artificial respiration on the surfboard

H. Other Specialized Equipment Rescues (depending on local use and need)

SUGGESTED COURSE OUTLINE FOR TRAINING SWIMMING POOL LIFEGUARDS

(Time allocation for each session is three hours)

SESSION I

A. Introductions (Management Representatives, Course Instructors, etc.)

B. Complete registration and/or application forms if not done prior to this session.

C. Check prerequisites (Chapter 1)

Note: Make arrangements well in advance of this session to have a physician on hand for physical examinations. The form to be used should provide space for the physician's signature and his answer to point "e."

D. Check swimming requirement (3) in pool (Chapter 1)

E. Advise those eligible and ineligible to continue the course.

F. Explain plans, schedule, etc., for remaining sessions of course.

Note: Encourage candidates to take notes. Provide notebooks or workbooks and pencils unless candidates were advised before this session to bring their own.

G. Lecture: The Ten Commandments of a Lifeguard (Chapter 1)

H. Lecture: The job of the lifeguard (Chapter 1)

Note: Emphasize the job description in your particular organization.

I. Lecture: personal health, fitness and in-service training (Chapter 2)

J. Questions and answers

K. Outside study assignment (if deemed necessary and if appropriate text or materials are provided or are available)

Note: If it is apparent that a large enrollment of candidates precludes the possibility of completing all items listed for Session I in a three-hour session, it is suggested that items B, C, D, E be scheduled and completed in a pre-course session or that these items constitute Session I of the course.

SESSION II

A. Check attendance (use your own method).

B. Review key points of previous session.

C. Discussion, oral or short written questions about study assignment

D. Lecture: Public relations (Chapter 2)

E. Lecture: Preventive lifeguarding (Chapter 3)

Note: Emphasize danger areas at your own facilities—cite accident and rescue statistics from your records.

F. Practical work in pool (Chapters 5, 6, 11)

1. Rescue equipment (pole, shepherd's crook, ring buoy, heaving line, emergency lights, lifeguard stands or chairs)

2. Rescue buoys, rescue tubes (large outdoor pools)

3. Whistles (when to use)

Note: Are whistles to be provided as part of each guard's uniform? If each lifeguard is expected to provide his own whistle, specify the type desired at your facility.

4. Whistle signals (have each lifeguard actually practice these)

Note: Individual and group practice with equipment and grading of each candidate's performance should be preceded by a thorough explanation and demonstration of equipment to be used at your facility.

5. Rescue buoys

6. Questions and answers

7. All swim, 500 yards (to increase endurance) check time

G. Assignment for next session

SESSION III (Chapter 8)

A. Check attendance.

B. Review key points of previous session.

C. Discussion, oral or short written questions about study assignments

D. Lecture and demonstrations

　　1. Drownings

　　2. Artificial respiration methods

　　3. Mechanical methods and devices

　　4. Other first-aid measures

　　5. First-aid supplies

Note: Devote maximum time to equipment and supplies to be used at your facility.

E. Practical work

　　1. Artificial respiration

　　2. Mechanical devices

Note: Following individual practice, stress "team" efforts by working in groups of twos, threes, etc.

F. Practical work in pool (Chapters 6, 8)

　　1. Mouth-to-mouth resuscitation in the water

　　2. Swimming rescues and assists without equipment

　　3. Questions and answers

　　4. All swim 500 yards (strive for faster time than in the previous session)

G. Assignment for next session

SESSION IV

A. Check attendance.

B. Review key points of previous session.

C. Discussion, oral or short written questions about study assignment

D. Lecture: Communications (Chapter 11)

Note: Demonstrate all communications equipment to be used at your facility.

E. Lecture: Cover-up systems (Chapter 12)

Note: Use blackboard or flip chart diagrams of systems to be employed at your facility.

F. Lecture: Body recovery (Chapter 9)

G. Practical work in pool

1. Hand signals, whistle signals, P. A. systems, etc.

2. Cover-up systems (Set up numerous simulated rescue situations. Rotate the lifeguards so that each will have practice in all locations, positions and circumstances.)

3. Individual and mass surface diving.

4. Questions and answers

H. Lecture and Demonstrations: Water conditions (Chapter 4)

Note: If the lifeguard's job responsibility includes the operation of filters, chlorinators, testing equipment, vacuuming, etc., it is recommended that an additional session be included prior to the last session of the course. Pages 52–56 of the text provide only a brief outline of these aspects of swimming pool operation. If the job responsibility includes only testing the water and/or using vacuum equipment, give appropriate instructions and individual practice in these procedures here, as part of Session V.

I. All swim 500 yards (reduce time)

J. Assignment for next session

SESSION V

A. Check attendance.

B. Review key points of previous session.

C. Discussion, oral questions about study assignment

D. Lecture: Legal aspects of lifeguarding (Chapter 13)

Note: Cite any past lawsuits from your own records.

E. Lecture: Records and reports (Chapter 14)

Note: Acquaint candidates with samples of all record and report forms to be used at your facility.

F. Lecture: Organization and regulations (Chapter 10)

Note: Emphasis • chain of command
- work schedules, pay scale and periods and other important aspects of your personnel policy
- rules for your pools
- budget (equipment costs money—insist upon good care and maintenance, etc.)

G. Final written examination

H. Practical work in pool
(Final skill tests)

Note: Explain plan or procedure for advising all candidates as to whether or not they passed the course.

Note: Give consideration to values of a "formal" graduation ceremony program including a presentation of certificates or diplomas.

Suggestions:
- Include demonstrations by the lifeguards.
- Invite parents and/or families of the lifeguards.
- Invite the public and local dignitaries.
- Distribute a printed program (include names of all course graduates, their instructors or "faculty"; your department [organization or municipal] officials, etc.).
- Arrange for appropriate publicity: news releases, pictures, etc.

RECOMMENDATIONS

A. Be prepared to begin a planned in-service training program as soon as your facilities are in operation and lifeguards are on the job.

B. As soon as possible after the completion of the lifeguard training course, conduct a thorough analysis or critique. Involve all persons who shared responsibilities—faculty or instructors (lecturers, demonstrators, examiners, etc.). Arrive at decisions regarding:

1. Length of course
2. Class or lesson time schedule (length and frequency)

3. Arrangement or sequence of subjects as outlined (lectures, demonstrations, practical work, etc.)

4. Where should more or less emphasis be placed?

C. Draft a training course outline that may be more applicable to your particular facilities or plan to follow this suggested outline again.

D. Keep striving for "top"-quality training. Utilize all resources in your locality to help achieve this goal.

E. Begin to develop potential candidates for future lifeguard training courses by frequent scheduling of senior lifesaving courses at your facilities. Schedule at least one that will be completed a week or two before the lifeguard course begins.

BIBLIOGRAPHY

American Red Cross. *First Aid*. Garden City, N. Y.: Doubleday & Co., Inc., 1957.

_____. *Life Saving and Water Safety*. Philadelphia: P. Blakiston's Son & Co., 1937.

"Artificial Respiration: The Holger Nielson Method." Lancet, July 1935.

Australia Surf Life Saving Handbook, 20th ed. The Surf Life Saving Association of Australia, 1957.

Boy Scouts of America. *Life Saving* in *Merit Badge Series*. New York: Boy Scouts of America, 1965.

_____. *Swimming, Water Sports, and Safety*. New York: Boy Scouts of America, 1938.

Craig, A. B., Jr. "Underwater Swimming and Loss of Consciousness." *Journal of the American Medical Association*, CLXXVI (April 1961).

Cureton, T. K., Jr. *Beginning and Intermediate National YMCA Progressive Aquatic Tests*. New York: Association Press, 1942.

_____. *How to Teach Swimming and Diving*. New York: Association Press, 1934.

Dill, D. B. "Symposium on Mouth-to-Mouth Resuscitation." *Journal of the American Medical Association*, CLXVII (May 17, 1958).

"Fatal Diving Injuries." Metropolitan Life Insurance Co. *Statistical Bulletin*, XX, No. 6 (June 1939).

Fowler, W. S. "Breaking Point of Breath Holding." *Journal of Applied Physiology*, 1954.

Friermood, H. T., ed. *New YMCA Aquatic Workbook*. New York: Association Press, 1964.

Gabrielson, B. W. "Facts on Drowning Accidents, Georgia." University of Georgia Printing Department, 1956.

Gordon, A. S. "Manual Artificial Respiration." *What's New: Abbott Laboratories*, CLXV (February 1952).

Karpovich, P. V. "Duration of Submersion in Drowning and Recovery." *Swimming Pool Data and Reference*, Annual 8 (1940).

————. "Problems in Drowning," *Journal of Physical Education,* XXXI (July–August 1934).

Lanoue, F. R. *Drownproofing.* Englewood Cliffs, N. J.: Prentice-Hall Inc., 1963.

————. "Some Facts on Swimming Cramps." *Research Quarterly,* XXI (1950).

New Zealand Surf Life Saving Association. *Official Handbook.* Wellington: McKenzie, Thornton, Cooper, Ltd., 1945.

Nicholis, C. P. A. *Beach Water Safety.* Los Angeles: Dept. of Playground and Recreation, 1939.

Pohl, H. F. "Lifesaving with the Surfboard." *Beach and Pool,* XVIII (November 1944).

Pohndorf, R. H. *Camp Waterfront Programs and Management.* New York: Association Press, 1960.

Royal Life Saving Society, The. *Handbook of Instruction,* 21st ed. London: The Royal Life Saving Society, 1946.

Safer, P. "Ventilatory Efficacy of Mouth-to-Mouth Artificial Respiration." *Journal of the American Medical Association,* CLXVII (May 17, 1958).

Sheffield, T. W. "The Art of Surfboarding." *Beach and Pool,* XX (September 1946).

————. "Evolution of Life Saving Services and Equipment." *Beach and Pool,* XIII (February, March and April 1939).

————. "Mechanics in Life Saving." *Beach and Pool,* X (May–June 1936).

Silvia, C. E. *Lifesaving and Water Safety Today.* New York: Association Press, 1965.

Weingarten, C. H., and Tanbenhaus, L. J. "Training of Rescue Personnel in Closed-Cardiac Resuscitation." *New England Journal of Medicine* CCLXX (June 1964).

SAMPLE FORMS

OPERATOR'S DAILY POOL REPORT

Day _____ Date _____
Weather _____ Temp. 10 a.m. _____ 4 p.m. _____
Water Temperature _____ Temp. 10 a.m. _____ 4 p.m. _____
                    Pool Attendance _____

RESULTS OF DAILY TESTS

pH of Water 10 a.m. _____   Chlorine Residual 10 a.m. _____
            12 a.m. _____   12 a.m. _____
             2 p.m. _____   2 p.m. _____
             4 p.m. _____   4 p.m. _____
             6 p.m. _____   6 p.m. _____
Physical Condition of Water _____

TREATMENT GIVEN

	Yes	No
Filters Washed	☐	☐
Deep Area Vacuumed	☐	☐
Any Sign of Algae?	☐	☐
Pool Surroundings Inspected	☐	☐
Dressing Area Inspected	☐	☐

CHEMICALS USED

New Water Added	_____	Gallons
Chlorine	_____	Pounds
HTH Granular or Tablets	_____	Pounds
Alkali:		
pH Plus	_____	Pounds
Soda Ash	_____	Pounds
Liquid Caustic Soda	_____	Pounds
Alum	_____	Pounds
Algeate	_____	Gallons
Super Algeate	_____	Gallons
Copper Sulphate	_____	Pounds
Celite	_____	Pounds

Remarks _____
_____

Operator sign { 1st Operator _____
                2nd Operator _____

OPERATOR'S DAILY POOL REPORT

(Continued)

SUPPLIES NEEDED

Chlorine 150 lb. Cy'l	_____	Test Set Solutions:	
105 lb. Cy'l	_____	Orthotolidine	_____
HTH Tablets	_____	Phenol Red	_____
HTH Granular	_____	Brom Thymol Blue	_____
Alkali:		Algeate	_____
pH Plus	_____	Super Algeate	_____
Soda Ash	_____	Herb-Tox Wd. Killer	_____
Liq. Caustic Soda	_____	U-Britener	_____
Alum	_____	AP Cleanser	_____
Anhydrous ammonia	_____	Hi-Tone	_____
Copper Sulphate	_____	Spar-San	_____
Celite	_____	Pestcide	_____
Filter-Kleen	_____	Unisoap	_____

BEACH PATROL DAILY LOG

DATE _____

PERSONNEL ON DUTY

Title	Name	On Duty	Off Duty	Sick Leave
Supervisor				
Captain				
Lieutenant				
Guard				
Guard				

WEATHER	10:00 A.M.	4:00 P.M.
Temperature		
Wind Direction		
Wind Strength		
Cloud Cover		
Water Temperature		
Surf Conditions		

Total daily attendance _____

Total rescues _____Police actions _____

Total first aid cases _____

Equipment lost or damaged _____

Unusual incidents _____

SWIMMING POOL REPORT

(This form must be completed and turned in to front office on Saturday)

Week of _____

	Mon.	Tues.	Wed.	Thur.	Fri.	Sat.
Number of hours pool water heater operated						
Number of hours pump and filters operated						
Time that filter was washed: No. 1						
No. 2						
No. 3						
Time required for washing filter: No. 1						
No. 2						
No. 3						
Pounds of filter material used						
Pounds of alum used						
Quantity of disinfectant used						
Pounds of Soda ash used						
Test No. 1 (Times of Test)						
Alkalinity						
Clearness of water						
Free Alum Test: Positive Negative						
Residual chlorine (p.p.m.)						
Temperature of air						
Temperature of water						
Test No. 2 (Times of Test)						
Alkalinity						
Clearness of water						
Free Alum Test: Positive Negative						
Residual chlorine (p.p.m.)						
Temperature of air						
Temperature of water						
Test No. 3 (Times of Test)						
Alkalinity						
Clearness of water						
Free Alum Test: Positive Negative						
Residual chlorine (p.p.m.)						
Temperature of air						
Temperature of water						
Volume of new water added (from meter)						
Time of cleaning pool						
Number of bathers: Afternoon						
Evening						
Total						
Number in Beginners' Class						
Pump motor oiled						
Fan and motor oiled						
Time required to clean pool						
Vacuum						
Backwash						

Remarks: (List Maintenance Work)

_____

Pool Attendant

FORMAL REPORT OF ACCIDENT

Date _____

Three typed copies of this report must be filed, one for the Unit Director and two for the Executive Director's Office, for every injury, no matter how trivial. Forms must be completed immediately after an injury occurs.

1. Victim's Name _____ Age_____

2. Address _____ Phone No._____

3. Place where accident occurred _____

4. Accident occurred on: Date_____ Day_____ Hour_____

5. Describe the accident _____

   _____

   _____

6. Was injured disobeying any rule or regulation in force at the time of the accident?_____ Was the injured negligent?_____ If so, in what way? _____

   _____

7. Supervisor in charge of activity at time of accident _____

8. Probable nature of injury _____

   _____

9. Nature of injury determined by _____

10. Persons present at the time of accident: Total Number_____

11. Names of those who saw accident _____ - _____

    _____ _____ _____ _____

12. What was done for the injured? _____

    _____

13. Was family notified? _____

    _____

14. Remarks _____

    _____

    _____

Report submitted by:

_____

_____
                                    Unit Director

Received by Executive Director on _____